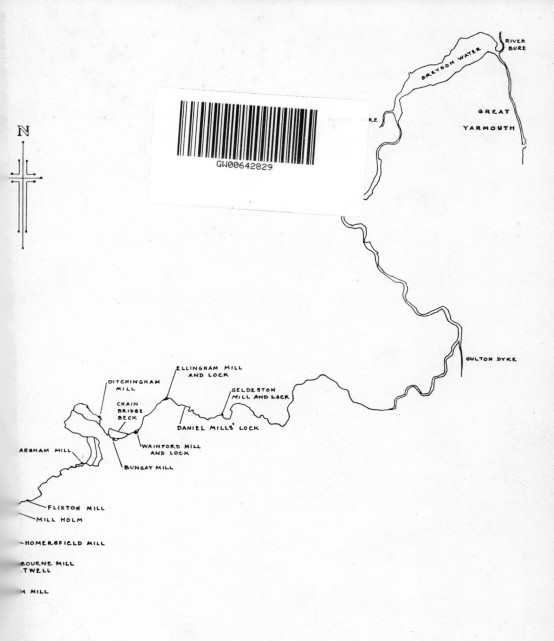

N

RIVER BURE

BREYDON WATER

GREAT YARMOUTH

RE

OULTON DYKE

ELLINGHAM MILL AND LOCK

DITCHINGHAM MILL

GELDESTON MILL AND LOCK

CHAIN BRIDGE BECK

DANIEL MILLS' LOCK

WAINFORD MILL AND LOCK

ARSHAM MILL

BUNGAY MILL

FLIXTON MILL

MILL HOLM

HOMERSFIELD MILL

BOURNE MILL
TWELL

M MILL

REF: ORDNANCE SURVEY
ONE - INCH MAPS
NOS. 126, 136 & 137.

THE RIVER WAVENEY, ITS WATERMILLS AND NAVIGATION

The River Waveney, Its Watermills and Navigation

by

DOUGLAS F PLUCK FRICS

FOREWORD
BY
DICK JOICE

Morrow & Co.
Bungay, Suffolk
1994

First published Morrow & Co., Bungay, Suffolk 1994
Copyright © Douglas F Pluck

ISBN O 948903 13 9

Typeset by Bungay Printers, 4b Market Place, Bungay
Printed & bound by Ipswich Book Co.

Contents

Diagrams

Endpapers: The River Waveney, Watermills and Locks

Between pages 13 and 14

Illustrations

Facing page

Facing pages

Acknowledgements

I am greatly indebted to many people for their interest and kind assistance in supplying information, for the loan of photographs and various documents and general encouragement without which this modest work would not have materialised and my notes would in all probability have remained in files.

My sincere thanks are especially due to the following:-

The late Mr. C.E. Aldridge of Barningham; the late Mr. Albert S. Bush of Needham; Mr. Hubert Bush of Needham, Dr. L.H. Cane, Curator of Bungay Museum; Mr. Frank E. Cannell of Bungay; Mr. D.W. Chaplin of Messrs. E.R. & F. Turner Ltd., of Ipswich; the late Miss Mary Daniels of Weybread; Mrs. Morton Denny of Harleston; Dr. Robert Dinn of Manchester University; Mr. Peter Dolman of Bramford, Ipswich; Mr. D.D. Dunkley of Messrs. Rank Hovis Ltd., Mr. George Durrant of Messrs. Durrants, Estate Agents, Harleston; Mr. E.G. Emms of Pulham Market, Mr. S.J. Govier of Hoxne; Mr. Ernest W.D. Hadingham of Holton; Mr. & the late Mrs. Fred Hadingham of Mendham; Mr. T.J. Harber of Earsham Mill; Dr. T.S. Hattersley of Ellingham Mill; Mr. & Mrs. John Howell of Mendham; Mr. F. Honeywood of Bungay; Mrs. Freda Jackson and Mr. Robert Jackson of Knutsford, Cheshire; Mr. A.F. Jermy of Bungay; Mr. Eric D. King of Bungay; Mrs. M. Martin of Downham Market; Mr. & Mrs. J.A. Naunton of Harleston; Mr. Arthur Pearce of Wortwell; Mr. K. Palmer of Homersfield; Mr. & Mrs. V.H. Robinson of Limbourne Mill, Wortwell; Mrs. L. Seaman of Attleborough; Mr. Robert Sharp of The Science Museum, London (for producing copies of the relevant section of the late Mr. H.E.S. Simmon's manuscript); Miss A. Pamela Taylor, Archivist, Arundel Castle Trustees Ltd.; Miss Margaret Thomas of Ellingham Mill; Mrs. Jean Turner late of Needham; Mr. R.M. Walker of Wells-next-the Sea; Mrs. D.J. Wooltorton of Wortwell; also the Archivists, Librarians and staff of the Ipswich, Lowestoft and Norwich Record Offices and the Diss and Harleston Libraries and Peter Morrow for kindly perusing my draft manuscript and making helpful suggestions.

If I have inadvertently omitted the name of anyone to whom my thanks are due, I offer my humble apologies.

Lastly my thanks are due in no small measure to my wife, Sheila, for her help and forbearance during my research and to my daughter, Elizabeth, for so ably typing and retyping the manuscript.

Foreword

'The River Waveney, its Watermills and Navigation' is the compelling title of Douglas Pluck's fascinating and comprehensive study of the milling industry down the ages in the Waveney valley. A Chartered Surveyor by profession and a more than keen amateur historian, the author is well equipped to research and record this account of one of the most interesting and important of man's achievements.

Starting with a brief history of watermills from the earliest Greek horizontal and Roman vertical mills which were introduced into Britain during the fourth and fifth centuries AD, there were no less than 5624 mills listed in the Domesday record of 1080. From there the author traces the development of water power and meticulously records the history of the fifteen mills that were working along the river Waveney. We learn about the construction of mills, the types of wheel in use (overshot, breastshot, and so on), the method of gearing and the transmission of power, we discover millstones, their composition, design and methods of dressing. We can study the navigation legislation for the control of the river water and realise how supremely important waterways such as the river Waveney were to the life of the area they served before the arrival of the railways and modern roads.

Glimpses into the everyday life of the miller can be revealing; we learn that millers retained a proportion of the flour as payment for grinding the wheat — the more unscrupulous ones growing rich in the process. Fire and flood were ever present hazards: in 1912 the miller's family had to be rescued by boat from the first floor of the mill cottage adjoining Needham Watermill, Suffolk during one of the Waveney's worst floods. Fire was responsible for the destruction of Weybread Mill in 1920; it was never rebuilt. The Munnings family of which the painter Alfred Munnings was a member, were associated with the mill at Mendham from 1872 to 1938. Eels were often a perquisite of the miller and the ones caught at Wortwell helped to pay the rent. Occasionally a miller might fall foul of the law, in one case the ecclesiastical kind, when in 1399, John Skilley, the Flixton miller, was imprisoned for seven years in the monastery at Langley for his 'wickedness of eating flesh on Fridays'.

The history of milling is a long and honourable one. The mill at Earsham was in continuous use on the same site since its mention in Domesday Book until 1982, over one thousand years! Sadly, of the remaining six watermills on the river Waveney, the mill at Ellingham (mentioned by the venerable Parson Woodforde in his diary for 1788) is now a Grade II listed building three others have been converted into dwellings and none are in working order.

Lastly, I would commend the Glossary, which is extensive and in itself makes fascinating reading. This is a most informative and well written account complemented by the line drawings and photographs which depict this lost industrial heritage. Altogether a noble description of a river and a way of life which survived floods, fire, drought and poor harvests over the centuries and was finally brought to a close by the winds of change, alternative sources of power and market forces.

Dick Joice

Introduction

I see the wealthy miller yet,
    His double chin, his portly size;
And who that knew him could forget
    The busy wrinkles round his eyes?
The slow, wise smile that round about
    His dusty forehead drily curled,
Seemed half within and half without,
    And full of dealings with the world.

In yonder chair I see him sit,
    Three fingers round the old silver cup —
I see his grey eyes twinkle yet
    At his own jest: grey eyes lit up
With summer lightnings of a soul
    So full of summer warmth, so glad,
So healthy, sound, and clean and whole,
    His memory scarce can make me sad.

Tennyson — *The Miller's Daughter.*

WITH AN INTEREST in Wind and Water mills spanning the past 30 or more years, it was, I suppose, natural that I should decide to take a slightly more than cursory look at the watermills along the River Waveney after returning to Norfolk in retirement. Perhaps more so, because as far as I can ascertain there is no publication devoted to this river's mills. In producing these notes I am very mindful of the short-comings of my efforts in this research. Nevertheless I trust I may have sown seeds of encouragement to others to pursue enquiries and thus to enlarge the picture of these old power-houses which have served the community so faithfully for very many generations.

Inevitably, in amateur research work of an industrial archaeological subject such as this, there is really no point of termination. In other words, there is no stage when it can be truthfully said that all the necessary information has been

1

collated. For various reasons, some all too obvious, it would have been inexpedient to have deferred dissemination of the facts procured to date.

The watermills along this river, like so many others were predominately cornmills but there were one or two whose power was utilised for the production of commodities other than flour or animal feed. These alternatives included linen, drabbett and paper.

Over the years, the mills were rebuilt, some as the result of fire. Enlargement and alterations in certain cases also took place. Furthermore modernisation was undertaken by the installation of roller plants and auxiliary power in the form of steam driven engines and later by diesel engines. The old form of lighting by candles and oil lamps was replaced by electricity which was also used to drive plant and machinery.

There are only four of the fifteen watermills along the River Waveney situated on the Norfolk side. The remainder are all on the Suffolk bank. This may be purely coincidental or there may well be a logical explanation for such a distribution. Perhaps the fact that Suffolk produced greater quantities of wheat is the answer to a larger proportion of the mills being sited on its southern side.

The mills varied in size as well as layout and part of their fascination lies in the fact that each possessed its own personality. They were designed and built by local craftsmen who confined their activities to a comparatively small area and incorporated their own ideas in each case. These were men who did not know how to do a job badly! The mill's appeal also is due to the fact that they were constructed of natural materials and were powered by an ancient and natural force. There is not the slightest incongruity of their place in the landscape, indeed it can be truthfully said that they add a measure of interest and beauty to the countryside. The same can also be said of windmills.

An examination of early photographs of some of these watermills in conjunction with the appropriate early twentieth century 25 inch Ordnance Survey maps, indicate that they varied in size; the largest being Earsham, Syleham, Mendham and Weybread. The smallest seems to have been Luck's. There was indeed a great output from the larger mills. They not only served the local community but considerable quantities of flour were conveyed by water transport to areas far afield, even overseas.

Various owners and occupiers of certain watermills on this river, as in other spheres, experienced business and financial difficulties at certain times, notwithstanding they were situated in the centre of a renowned and so-called prosperous corn-growing area. A number were forced into bankruptcy with the inevitable traumatic consequences, although the exact reasons for such turns of events are not readily available. However, it is interesting to note the bankruptcy notices referring to seven of these mills (and the subsequent sale notices), were published in the late 18th century and during the first half of the 19th century. One or two of the mills also suffered somewhat tragic events of a different nature during their working lives, the details of which are related in the following notes.

In later times certain of the Waveney mills were considered to be worthwhile propositions from an economic point of view by both non-milling owners and miller occupiers. Apart from being updated with machinery, they were enlarged and improved, such was the case with Mendham, Earsham and Ellingham mills. Those that were destroyed or badly damaged by fire, were, in certain cases, thought to be worth rebuilding, e.g. Needham and Bungay. In these two cases brick was used with cast-iron windows and cast-iron stanchions were incorporated in the Bungay mill. Syleham and Weybread were two mills, however, that were not rebuilt after being completely destroyed by fire. It is said that the owner of the latter mill was not insured against fire at the time of the incident and coupled with the fact that sales of flour were extremely poor at that time, may well be more than adequate reasons for the mill being lost forever.

Fortunately there are now several watermills and windmills throughout the country which have been restored to working order and some are operating on a commercial basis. Many are open to the public and a visit to these truly delightful and wonderful mechanical devices of yesterday's world will, without doubt, prove very rewarding. However, it is to be noted that those watermills that remain along the River Waveney are all privately owned and are not open to the public.

In March 1987 The Traditional Cornmillers Guild was formed by a group of independent wind and water millers. Not only do they use a natural force to power their mills but they produce unadulterated stoneground meals and flours.

It is far from my intention that this unobstrusive book should be looked upon as a quasi learned treatise. It is only too obvious it is not. It was not produced with the specialist or professional molinologist in mind — but for the more local or casual reader who, it is hoped, will perhaps discover an interest in this section of industrial archaeology.

D.F.P.

Watermills
A Brief Commentary

"The water mill was the parent of modern industry."
George Long.

The discovery of water power and its application to grind corn through the medium of a small primitive mill, apart from assisting and even reducing man's labours, was in effect a revolution of no small measure. It lead the way, through development, to a partially industrialised society, albeit primitive in those very early times.

The earliest reference to a watermill is usually taken to be that by the Greek poet Antipater of Thessalonica in his epigram written around 85BC. Of course there could have been a form of watermill in existence prior to that date. The next early mention of a watermill is by Strabo, the Greek chronicler, when he refers to one belonging to Mithridates, King of Pontus in Asia; the mill being discovered in 65BC, after the King was defeated by the Romans.

Both these writers in all probability were referring to a primitive type of mill of simple operation which became known as the Greek mill. It comprised a horizontal wheel mounted at the base of an upright or vertical shaft. There was no gearing and the upper end of the shaft was fitted into the upper or runner stone by means of wedges after passing through the lower or bed stone. Around the rim of the wheel blades or paddles were fitted and set at an angle. By means of a trough or channel water was directed on to the paddles and the force of the water caused the wheel to rotate. It will be seen that one revolution of the wheel gave one revolution of the shaft and upper stone. These mills were, as is shown by diagram A, of simple construction, low-powered and slow grinding. Grain was fed into the eye of the upper stone from a hopper via a spout. The lower end of the vertical shaft was held in a bearing fixed to a beam, known as the tenter beam. This beam could be adjusted by wedges in the very early mills or in later mills by a 'lightening tree' so as to adjust the gap between the stones. These small mills served the rural communities for many centuries.

Eventually the Greek mill spread further afield and into Europe and Scandinavia where the design of the horizontal wheel and particularly the

4

paddles varied. One variation of the Greek wheel had deeper paddles set directly into a hub at the base of the shaft. Such wheels were to be found in the Shetlands and Scandinavia as well as in parts of Europe where they were often referred to as the Norse mill. The Greek or Norse mill was in use up to fairly recent times in Scotland, Ireland and Portugal. It will be seen that this early type of mill was really the forerunner of the modern turbine.

Next came what is generally referred to as the Vertical Mill. The Roman architect and engineer, Marcus Vitruvius, described it in his treatise 'De Architectura,' written during the years 20BC and 11BC, and he may possibly have invented this design of mill himself. This watermill was henceforth known as the Roman mill. Here, we see the introduction of gears, probably for the first time in a mill. Its wheel was mounted vertically on a horizontal shaft and it incorporated a simple gear arrangement. Diagram B is a representation of the watermill described by Vitruvius. The waterwheel itself is external and fitted with paddles. The shaft on which it is mounted is comparatively short thus the torque is virtually eliminated. On the end of the shaft a toothed tympanum or drum is fixed in a vertical position which is in mesh with a larger toothed tympanum or drum fixed horizontally at the top of an upright shaft and immediately beneath the pair of stones. The top of the upright shaft is taken through the lower stone and is mortised into the upper or runner stone. A similar gear arrangement is shown in an illustration of a medieval Roman mill except that the vertical tympanum is replaced by a lantern pinion. In Ramelli's illustration of 1588 the undershot mill is shown to have an extra pair of gears, the great spur wheel having a double row of pegs or cogs. In all these mills grain was fed into the stones by a suspended hopper placed above.

The Roman mill was the forerunner of our more modern watermill of the 19th and 20th centuries. The Romans may have introduced the vertical watermill into this country although there is no conclusive evidence that they did. However the introduction would not have been earlier than 398 AD, nor later than 448 AD, the year they abandoned Britain. Eventually the vertical or Roman mill became established in this country and was generally adopted by the Saxons. Although the Greek or Norse mill continued to be used until fairly recent times, especially in mountainous regions, it was in effect supplanted by the somewhat more powerful Roman watermill.

The earliest authentic reference to a watermill in England occurred in Anglo-Saxon times in a charter of 762 AD, whereby Ethlebert of Kent granted the use of a mill belonging to a monastery in a district on the east side of the city of Dover. There is an even earlier authentic mention of a watermill in Ireland which relates to the year 651 AD.

Dr. Richard Holt, a Research Fellow in the Department of Medieval History at the University of Birmingham, wrote an article entitled: "Milling Technology in the Middle Ages : The Direction of Recent Research". It was published in the Industrial Archaeology Review, Volume XIII Number 1 Autumn 1990. On page 52 of the Review Richard Holt relates an interesting set of facts concerning early references to watermills. He says: "And not surprisingly, archaeology points to an even earlier use of the mill by the English, with a firm date in the 690's now having been assigned to the massive and sophisticated machine excavated in the 1950's at Old Windsor on the Thames". Also, "It is the preservation of ancient timbers that has ensured we know more about the Irish mills of this period than we do about those of the rest of Europe. The earliest mill so far discovered there has been reliably dated to the years around 630, and the evidence of the early law codes is that already by that date the watermill was a long-established feature of Irish life." These references are to Vertical watermills.

In the year of 1080 the Domesday Survey was commenced and completed in 1086. A total of 5624 mills are listed. These were all or mainly watermills as windmills did not appear until about one hundred years later. The earliest references to windmills being in 1185 to one at Weedley in Yorkshire and 1191 to one near Bury St. Edmunds in Suffolk. Only the word mill (moliñ) is used in the survey. It is therefore likely that in certain cases it could refer to an animal-powered mill or even a hand-mill. It is also to be noted the survey did not cover the whole of the country. No mills are listed for Cumbria, Durham, Lancashire or Northumbria. This is not to say there were no mills in these counties — they were just not included in the survey. In Norfolk there were 731 Domesday Settlements and mills are mentioned as existing in 302 of them. Domesday Settlements in Suffolk amounted to 640 of which 178 had mills therein.

The word mill throughout the survey is unlikely to have referred to a building but is generally taken to describe one pair of stones. Thus if there were two pairs of stones under one roof the survey would list two mills. It will also be seen that in some settlements fractions of mills are listed. This indicates a mill was shared between two or more settlements.

Another interesting point is that in the Domesday Survey there are five mills listed in Suffolk as "Winter Mills" (molinum hiemale), but none in Norfolk. Such mills were considered not to be worth so much from a rental or tax point of view as they could only be worked in winter months. They were situated on comparatively small streams which had only sufficient flow of water in winter time to turn the wheels.

In medieval times many watermills were owned by the various monastic orders but a great many were also owned by lords of the manor, indeed throughout this lengthy period each manor possessed a mill. Tenants of the lords were forbidden the use of hand querns, indeed possession of them was prohibited. In order to make certain manorial mills were fully employed, tenants were forced to have their corn ground at such mills in return for a toll.

In the event this singularly unfair imposition was strongly resented which resulted in ceaseless friction between the parties. Obviously the tenants preferred to use their own querns or hand mills and thus retain all their flour for themselves. At times feelings ran high to put it mildly. A case in point concerns the Abbot of St. Alban's Abbey, Cirencester. Here, around 1274, the Abbot as lord of the manor, started to demand the surrender of hand mills of local citizens and eventually he had their homes searched resulting in a number being discovered in use. These he confiscated and had them brought to the Abbey where they were used as paving stones!

Gradually, and as the years passed, more and more landlords let out their mills to tenant millers and, as payment for grinding customers' corn, a portion of the grain was retained. Such a means of payment was often abused and not without reason the miller was frequently accused of cheating; feelings being amply summed up by the old rhyme:

> "Miller-dee, miller-dee, dusty poll,
> How many sacks of flour hast thou stole?
> In goes a bushel; out comes a peck!
> Hang old miller-dee up by his neck!"

Moving forward to more modern times, a story on this theme related by Mr. Ernest Knights of Harleston (of Messrs. E.H. Knights & Sons Ltd., Agricultural Engineers and formerly Milling Engineers and Millwrights of Harleston) and published in the East Anglian Magazine of August 1972, is as follows:-

'In pre-war days a prosperous miller and merchant always preferred large American cars, which he changed regularly. One of his elderly farmer customers watched him step out of a brand new Buick at a local market and said:

> "I see you've got another new motor, Charles."
> "Yes, William."
> "A real big one this time."
> "Yes, William, I like a big car."
> "Ow," said the farmer, "I s'pose I'll hetta pay for ut."
> "Oh no, William, — no — you've already done that!"

The early mills were of all wood construction, including the gears of the Vitruvian mill, indeed even the gearing of very much later mills were constructed of wood. Axles were invariably of oak as were the gear wheels, although occasionally beech, elm and hornbeam were used. The wooden cogs or teeth were made of quite a variety of hardwoods, including apple, pear, beech, box, hornbeam and holly. Early waterwheels were usually of oak construction with elm paddles.

Later cast iron was used for both water wheels and gear wheels. John Smeaton (1724–1792), the first man to call himself a "civil" engineer, greatly improved the efficiency of water wheels and the gearing in mills from 1769 onwards by the use of metal. In 1769 he invented the cast iron axle replacing those of oak which had been used for centuries in watermills. In 1770 he invented cast iron shrouds (the outer casing on the sides of the water wheel which enclosed the buckets) and in 1778 he introduced cast iron gearing. Then in 1780 he used wrought iron for buckets (the fittings around the waterwheel which held the water).

Wooden waterwheels were either compass arm or clasp arm construction. In the former spokes were morticed into the axle and as there were a number of mortises inevitably this was a weak point of the axle. Furthermore, this type of wheel was not easy to balance and adjust. In the case of the clasp arm wheel, there were two pairs of spokes or arms, each pair clasping the sides of the axle, the ends being fitted to the rim. The pairs of arms were set at right angles to each other and the wheel was adjusted by wedges being driven in between the axle and arms. The clasp arm wheel was preferred by mill wrights and in any event this particular type of waterwheel was easier to repair and adjust.

Waterwheels were often a mixture of wooden and metal construction. These so-called composite wheels had a casing fitted to the square shaped axle into which the wooden spokes were fitted. The outer ends of the spokes were then fitted into a metal rim casting. The composite wheels had a reasonably long life and were also better balanced. The all metal wheel was, in the early models, made up of cast iron parts bolted together. Later these wheels were made up of complete sections, usually four, i.e., a quarter of the rim, spokes and a quarter of the axle boss, all bolted together.

The section of the stream which runs up to the waterwheel is termed the "mill-race" or "leat" and the water carried away from the wheel is called the "tail race". Waterwheels were given descriptive names after the manner in which the water strikes or enters them. (See Diagram C). The Undershot wheel is worked by kinetic energy, i.e., by the speed of the water flowing on to the wheel. They were easy to construct and maintain but had a somewhat low efficiency. Smeaton considered their maximum theoretical efficiency to be 22 per cent.

The undershot waterwheel was improved by a French General, J.V. Poncelet, and introduced about 1824. In the Poncelet wheel, water was guided down a 1:10 slope and forced into curved iron buckets. This was achieved by the use of an inclined hatch of between 40° and 60°. A false board held back a head of water at the top and the bottom gate was adjusted by a hand wheel which was often inside the mill. The miller could therefore make adjustments to control the water from inside his mill. Theoretical efficiency was increased with this wheel to between 65 and 70 per cent. This wheel had a high rotational speed and was ideal for corn grinding and paper making.

The Breast Shot wheel was actuated by potential energy, i.e. gravity or the weight of the water. Such wheels had buckets which were designed to hold as much water for as long as possible. The amount of water running on to these wheels was controlled by a vertical hatch. Water entered the buckets at a point level with the axle. There were also low and high breast shot wheels. In the case of the former, it was really both a potential and kinetic wheel. The relative theoretical efficiencies were 35 per cent (low breast), 45 per cent (breast) and 55 per cent (high breast).

Overshot wheels were considered to be the most powerful. Water was taken to the wheel by means of a launder or trough to a point just past top dead centre. It was therefore worked entirely by potential energy and Smeaton estimated the theoretical efficiency of these wheels to be a maximum of 63 per cent. The flow of water on to the wheel could be controlled by a gate or hatch located on the launder. There was however a problem when the water rose in the tail race or when there was a flood. Since the bottom of the wheel turned in the opposite direction to the flow of the water the wheel would be slowed down or stopped. This could be avoided by making sure the bottom of the wheel was always above the highest level of water likely in the tail race or by simply lowering the floor of the tail race to the requisite level.

Lastly there was the Pitchback wheel, considered to be almost comparable in power to the overshot wheel. It too was operated by potential energy, the water again being taken on to the wheel via a launder to a point just before top dead centre. It is to be noted that the wheel turned in the same direction as the flow of water in the tail race. Pitchback wheels had a theoretical efficiency of about 60 per cent.

During the 19th century, and even during the early part of the 20th century, waterwheels were sometimes replaced by turbines, very often when or after a roller plant was installed. Three of the Waveney mills had turbines fitted: they were Earsham, Wainford and Ellingham. The turbine fitted to Earsham mill, in spite of being installed by the well-known and respected firm Gilkes & Gordon of Kendall, was taken out after it was found the original water-wheel was superior in performance; so the waterwheel went back. This firm's first turbine was built in 1856 so the turbine fitted in Earsham mill must have been some time after that date. The efficiency of water turbines were calculated to be in excess of 80 per cent but as installation involved an appreciable capital sum only a comparatively small number of mills indulged in such a changeover. Those that did were obviously very viable concerns.

The arrangement of machinery inside watermills varied in detail from mill to mill but the layout conformed to one of two basic forms as shown in Diagrams D and E. The difference between these two layouts is the manner in which the power from the waterwheel was transmitted to drive the mill stones.

The first of these arrangements, and that found more frequently in mills, was by gears arranged around a great spur wheel. Here the drive from the waterwheel is taken to the mill stones via a pitwheel and bevel gear known as the wallower, fitted to the lower end of an upright shaft, and a great spur wheel which was in mesh with the stone nuts. At the top end of the upright shaft was a bevel gear known as the crown wheel. Power to a layshaft or layshafts was taken from this latter gear to drive machinery by pulleys and belts. Depending upon the power of the waterwheel and the diameter of the great spur wheel, there could be from two to four pairs of stones. The second and less usual layout was by bevel gears from a layshaft. In this case the drive from the waterwheel is again via a pitwheel and plain or simple gears to a horizontal layshaft on which bevel gears are mounted and these were in mesh with stone nuts. As will be seen almost any number of stones could be driven from such an arrangement. The only watermill on the River Waveney, which had a layshaft layout was that at Homersfield. The stones could be driven either from above (overdrift), which was the customary arrangement, or from below (underdrift), in the latter case the stone spindle would be taken through the lower, bed or stationary stones. The stones are enclosed in a wooden casing known as a vat or tun above which is mounted a hopper into which grain is fed from the bin floor (above). The grain is then passed in to the stones via the shoe.

Transmission of power from a turbine and its upright shaft was often by belt drives to the stone spindles. When a roller plant was installed belt drive was the normal form of power transmission from horizontal shafts or layshafts.

Other equipment usually installed in watermills included:-

Tentering Gear, for adjusting and regulating the distance between the stones; (see Diagram F)

Smutter, a machine for removing dirt, smut and diseased particles from wheat;

Reel Separator or Separator, equipment for cleaning grain;

Aspirator, a device for cleaning grain;

Wire Machine, a rotary sifting device having a stationary wire mesh cylinder swept internally by revolving brushes;

Jog-Scry (Joggling Screen), an inclined oscillating sieve for sifting partly ground corn before a second grinding — also called a Jumper;

Plansifter, equipment for sieving flour;

Bolter, a device with a silk covered wooden cylinder for dressing flour out of meal;

Centrifugal Reel Separator, a device for dressing flour; (See Illustration Diagram G from an early twentieth century catalogue of Henry Simon Ltd., Manchester);

Dresser, a device for grading flour;

Temise*, a sieve used to produce fine flour;

All the above machines and equipment were powered by the waterwheel or turbine via layshafts, pulleys and belts. Later when additional or auxiliary power was installed in the form of a steam, diesel or oil engine then invariably such auxiliary power was utilised to drive the cleaning, dressing and grading machinery.

Sacks of corn were stored on the top or garner floor of the mill and the means of transporting them there was by a device known as the sack hoist. (See Diagram H). This was a simple but ingenious idea and various methods of operating the hoist were used. The most popular system was by the slack and tight belt principle. A drum or barrel on which a chain was wound was supported at one end by a fixed bearing. At the other end was a pulley or flanged wheel and a bearing mounted on a moveable beam which could be moved vertically by means of a control rope via a lever. The drive was taken from a layshaft and belt to the pulley on the barrel. When the hoist was not in use the barrel dropped thus slackening the belt.

The chain was run from the barrel through a hole in each pair of trap doors, located in the floors below, to the ground floor. The end of the chain was looped round the neck of the sack of corn and a gentle pull on the control rope, which also ran down to the ground floor, operated the lever which in turn tightened the belt and then the barrel would revolve winding on the chain and lifting the sack through the hinged trap doors to the top floor.

Millstones are made from a variety of substances. The best type of stones for grinding wheat were known as French Burrs. The material in this case was a freshwater quartz quarried from the Paris basin at La Ferté-sous-Jouare, seventy kilometers east of Paris and at Epernon, sixty kilometers west of Paris.

This particular stone was quarried in small pieces, graded and trimmed to fit together and form a complete stone of even quality. The pieces were cemented together with plaster of Paris and bound with an iron hoop round the circumference. The working faces of the stones were dressed in the manner shown in Diagram I and the back of these stones was rendered smooth by the application of cement.

Another type of stone, known as Derbyshire Peaks, were hewn in one piece from the solid rock of Millstone Grit found in the north-eastern parts of Derbyshire and south-west Yorkshire. A visitor to these areas will find several complete or partly cut stones lying around no longer required. These Millstone Grit stones are of the sandstone variety and so are much softer than the French Burr stones. They were mainly used for grinding cattle grist; also barley, oats, peas and beans.

* Temise is pronounced Thames. Thus the saying "you will never set the Thames on fire," is really referring to a Temise, i.e. a sieve and not the river, and indicates the person using the sieve is shaking it slowly!

Stones of a volcanic origin were also used. Known as "cullen" stones, from Cologne, they were used on occasions for wheat. Although preferable to Derbyshire Peaks, they were superceded by French Burrs during the nineteenth century. There were stones made from a similar kind of lava rock which was quarried from the Andernach and Koblenz areas of Germany.

Composition stones were also used. These consisted of ground particles of stone or emery embedded in cement and the composition was then set on a cast iron backing plate.

Milling stones varied in diameter from 2ft 6 ins to 5ft, but the most popular sizes were 3ft 6ins and 4ft.

The surface of stones had to be dressed and this was done by hand. Diagram I shows the usual form of dressing for a 4ft diameter pair of stones. The output from stones depended upon their size, the larger diameter stones were run slowly in comparison. The following table will give an indication of the relationship between the size of the stones, the number of revolutions per minute of the runner stone and the quantity produced per hour:

Diameter of Stones	3'0"	3'6"	4'0"
Revolutions per minute	180	150	130
Bushels of flour per hour	$3^1/_4$	4	5
Bushels of animal feed per hour	$6^1/_2$	8	10

In order to dress the stones it was necessary to raise the upper or runner stone from the lower or bed stone, turn it over and lower it to the floor. Stones being somewhat heavy were not easy to handle. A new stone 3'6" diameter and 8 or more inches thick could weigh around 12cwts., whereas a 4'0" diameter stone would weight about 17cwts. Although in very early days this operation was effected by the use of iron and wooden wedges and a rope, later a much easier method was adopted. The equipment consisted of an iron gibbet and calipers which amounted to a simple form of crane. A lug at the end of each caliper arm fitted into a hole in the side of the runner stone, the calipers being lowered and raised from the gibbet by means of a vertical screw which passes through the top of the gibbet. The stone could therefore be raised by means of the screw and turned over through the lugs on the calipers.

Mill stones needed balancing and this was achieved by the use of four balancing boxes, usually cast iron, inserted into the back of the runner stone close to the outer edge or skirt. The boxes were at 90° to each other and lead weights were placed inside them. The lead weights were invariably odd pieces of lead, the amount of which could easily be varied so as to obtain the required balance.

In the 1870's roller milling was introduced and in order to remain viable a number of millers installed a roller plant. To begin with it was often a partial plant — as was the case with Mendham Mill which later, in 1905, had a complete Turner 3-sack roller plant installed. Limbourne was another mill which ran both stones and rollers as it had a $^1/_2$ sack roller plant. The public demand for white flour, itself brought about by the roller milling system, meant that by the 1890's a great many medium sized mills and all the larger mills had adopted this new system of milling.

A roller mill is a machine which has one or more pairs of rollers, the latter being made from a "special mixture of metal for the chilled iron rolls." The rolls were either smooth or fluted and the roller mill itself was driven from a layshaft by a belt and pulleys. (See illustration and Diagram J from an early twentieth century catalogue of Henry Simon Ltd., Manchester). In many cases the waterwheel did not provide sufficient power to drive a roller mill and whilst they were sometimes replaced by water turbines, as often as not such mills were powered by steam engines. The replacement of water power with steam power meant that mills no longer had to occupy rural sites by the side of or over a stream or river. They could be sited where communications were more favourable or close to or even at ports where grain from abroad could be delivered direct to the mill.

Those mills which did not have roller mills installed, either because the volume of trade did not justify such equipment, or because the miller could not afford the expensive machinery, usually went over to provender milling, i.e., grinding for animal feed, or, alas closed down forever.

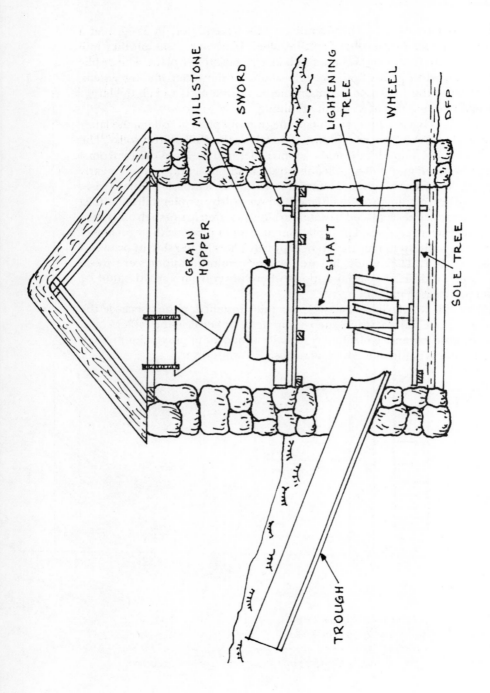

MILLSTONE

SWORD

LIGHTENING TREE

WHEEL

DFP

GRAIN HOPPER

SHAFT

SOLE TREE

TROUGH

Diagram A

A Shetland or Norse Mill

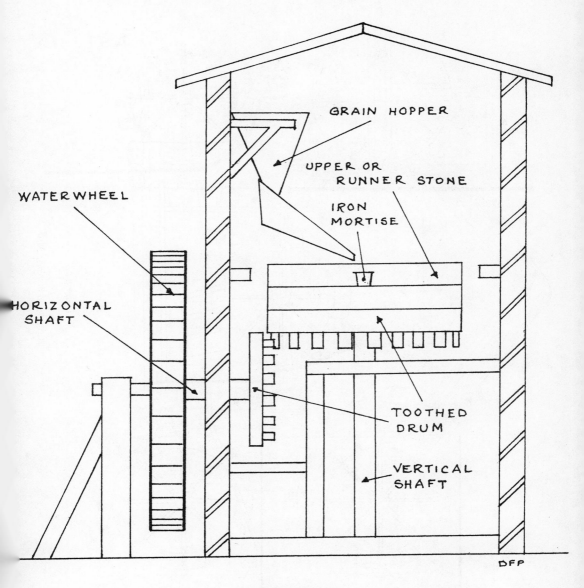

GRAIN HOPPER

UPPER OR
RUNNER STONE

IRON
MORTISE

WATERWHEEL

HORIZONTAL
SHAFT

TOOTHED
DRUM

VERTICAL
SHAFT

DFP

Diagram B

This diagram, is based on one drawn by William Newton (1735 – 1790), architect and translator, from the Latin, of Vitruvius's treatise, <u>De Architectura</u>. It shows the drive to the upper stone. The toothed drums (or typani) of different size allow the millstone to revolve more slowly than the waterwheel, thus allowing for use on a fast flowing stream.

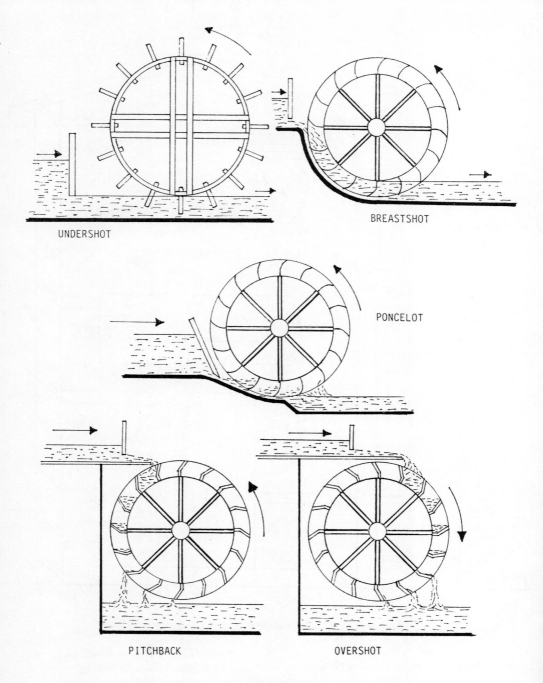

UNDERSHOT

BREASTSHOT

PONCELOT

PITCHBACK

OVERSHOT

Diagram C

Type of Waterwheels

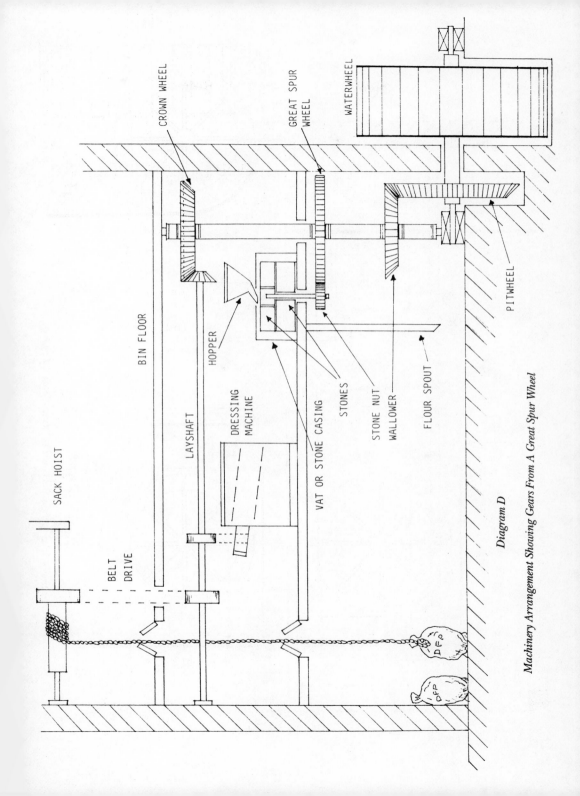

Diagram D

Machinery Arrangement Showing Gears From A Great Spur Wheel

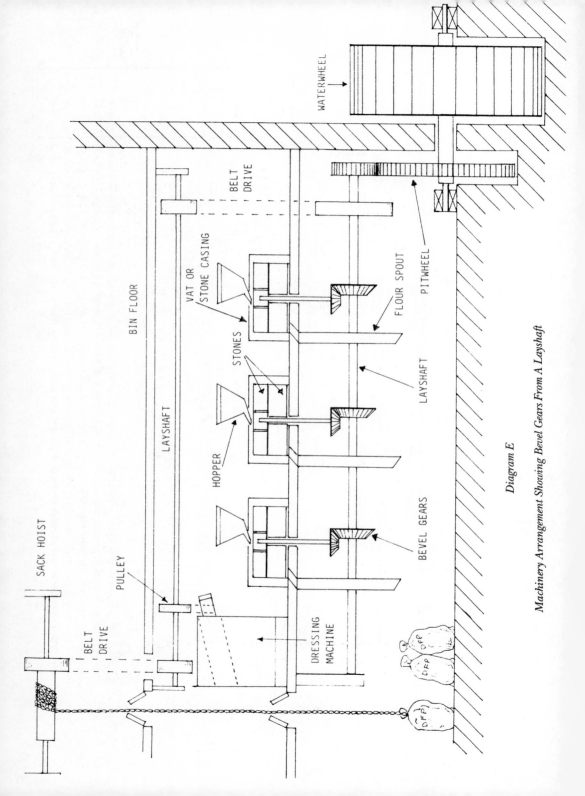

WATERWHEEL

BELT DRIVE

BIN FLOOR

LAYSHAFT

VAT OR STONE CASING

STONES

HOPPER

PULLEY

SACK HOIST

BELT DRIVE

DRESSING MACHINE

FLOUR SPOUT

PITWHEEL

LAYSHAFT

BEVEL GEARS

Diagram E

Machinery Arrangement Showing Bevel Gears From A Layshaft

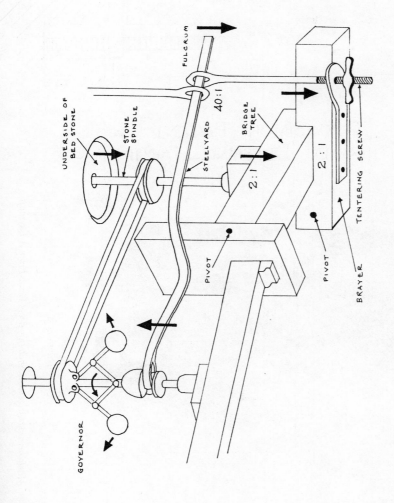

UNDERSIDE OF
BED STONE

STONE
SPINDLE

FULCRUM

STEELYARD

40:1

BRIDGE
TREE

2:1

2:1

PIVOT

PIVOT

BRAYER

TENTERING SCREW

GOVERNOR

Diagram F

The tentering screw is used to set the gap between the stones but to ensure consistent grinding, the gap between the millstones needs to remain constant. Variations in waterwheel speed cause this gap to alter. This is countered by operation of the tentering gear. The sleeve of the governor is altered by the cylindrical lead weights flying out or dropping with variations in the speed of the stone spindle. In turn the steelyard moves up or down thus changing the position of the brayer and bridge tree. As the base of the stone spindle rests upon the latter then the runner stone will either be raised or lowered and so the distance between the stones is automatically adjusted to that required.

THE "SIMON" PATENT
CENTRIFUGAL DRESSING MACHINE.

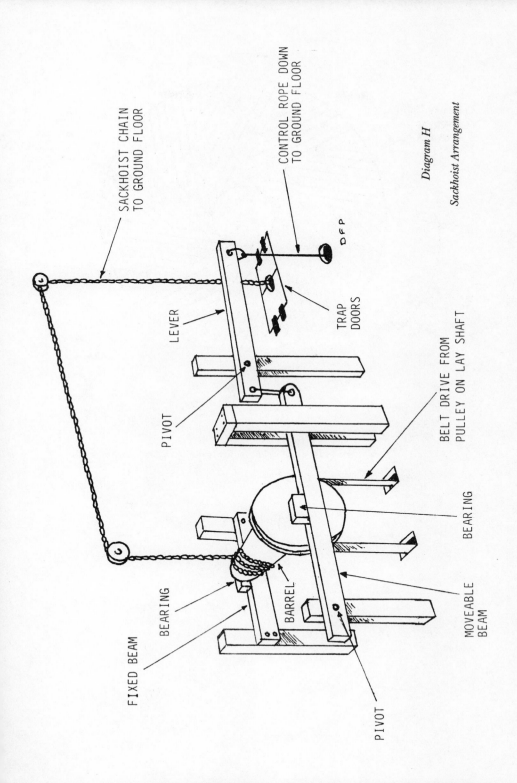

SACKHOIST CHAIN
TO GROUND FLOOR

CONTROL ROPE DOWN
TO GROUND FLOOR

D F P

LEVER

PIVOT

TRAP
DOORS

BELT DRIVE FROM
PULLEY ON LAY SHAFT

BEARING

FIXED BEAM

BEARING

BARREL

MOVEABLE
BEAM

PIVOT

Diagram H

Sackhoist Arrangement

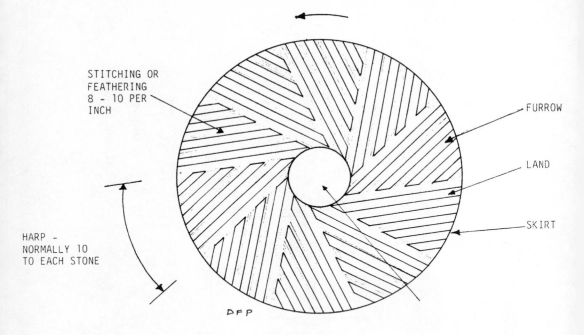

STITCHING OR
FEATHERING
8 - 10 PER
INCH

FURROW

LAND

SKIRT

HARP -
NORMALLY 10
TO EACH STONE

DFP

Diagram I

Typical Form of Dressing a 4 Foot Diameter French Burr Millstone

The "Reform"
Four-High Roller Mill.

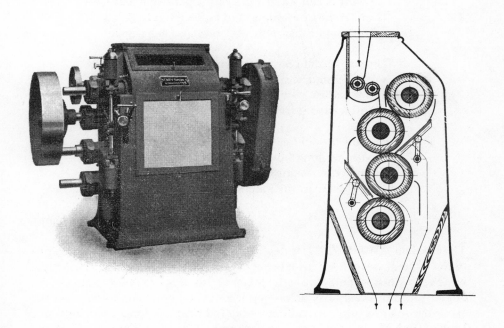

The River Waveney and its Navigation

Sweet dream of my childhood! Still Fancy will fly
   To thy green sunny vales with a pensive delight;
There Memory wanders, and pours forth her sigh
   To the spot that no longer may gladden my sight.

Thy soft verdant meadows, when spring was at hand.
   Were tinted with tenderer, lovelier green;
At her earliest visit each bud would expand,
   And vary with fresh opening beauties the scene.

How my bosom has bounded when summer drew near,
   With her long sunny season so balmy and mild;
Oh, ne'er to my spirit was summer so dear,
   As when O'er thy waters, sweet Waveney! she smiled.

From Poems by Agnes Strickland.

The late James Wentworth Day described the Waveney "as a gentlemanly sort of river. Quiet, peaceful, lit with beauty, born in the deep heart of East Anglia, enriched by history and alive with birds and fish. It is a river for the artist, the angler and the small boat sailor who likes peace upon the waters. On the Waveney one can catch, in sudden visions of beauty, the space and light, the background of water, woods, marshes and reeds that is the secret of the Norwich school of painters from "Old Crome" right through to Roland Green and Seago — sudden nuances of sunlit green, translucent effects of light and wind and sun, with splashes of vivid colour that for a second of time rival anything you may see on the Mediterranean." Unfortunately he makes no mention of the watermills which for centuries formed a most important part of the Waveney scene. Indeed they created a great deal of life and history on this ancient river. Likewise with the River's Navigation which, through all it's vicissitudes and chequered career over some 260 or so years, added in no small measure a special life and scene with the majestic and distinctive wherries plying between Bungay and Yarmouth.

The area through which the Waveney flows north-eastwards is a flat alluvial plain. It is bordered by marshes throughout the vast majority of its course and like other East Anglian rivers is comparatively slow moving.

The Waveney, whose anglo-saxon name was Wafien, meaning "waving or troubled waters" rises in swampy ground about $1\frac{1}{2}$ miles south of South Lopham near Diss, and about $\frac{3}{4}$ mile NW of Redgrave (NGR TM 03957900) where the B1113 road from Kenninghall to Botesdale crosses the valley. At the same spot, just across the road, the Little Ouse rises and flows in a westerly direction. These two rivers form the boundary between Norfolk and Suffolk, the Waveney finishing by running into Breydon Water at Burgh Castle west of Great Yarmouth. The Waveney was not in fact called upon to act as a boundary until the See of East Anglia was divided at the Synod of Hereford in 673 AD.

In 1877, the Select Committee of the House of Lords on Conservancy Boards, published a Report and at Appendix B thereof, p.p. 282–6, the River Waveney is shown as being one of "The Principal Rivers of England and Wales" having a length of $58\frac{3}{4}$ miles and a Catchment Basin of 339 square miles. As its area of basin is between 100 and 500 square miles, it is scheduled in the Appendix as "Third Class".

The Waveney is not in normal times a fast flowing river and this is evidenced by the fact that in 1878 a Mr. J. Teasdale surveyed the river for the Waveney Valley Drainage Commissioners and found a fall of about 67 feet between Hoxne Mill and Beccles Bridge — a distance of some 25 miles. This gives an average fall of one foot in about 1,970 feet. The average width of the Waveney "is said to be about 100 feet." [1]

In his book, "The History of Suffolk," the Revd. J.J. Raven, D.D., F.S.A., states, "The fall from Hoxne Mill to Yarmouth Harbour is only 80 feet, a fact which speaks for itself." In spite of these implications, the Waveney has supplied sufficient power to the several mills on its banks for at least 900 years. Dr. Raven also says that the Waveney "first feels the pulse of the North Sea at spring-tide about Shipmeadow Lock."

In ancient times Waveney was written "Avona" and it appears that "Waveney" was a corruption thereof. (The town of Bungay was also formerly known by the name of Avona). It is possible that in the distant past the river was navigable up to Weybread since an anchor was found in the bed of the tributary which runs into the Waveney at this village. Admittedly this is far from conclusive evidence. However, even up to the earlier part of the 20th century, the Waveney was navigable by wherry up to Bungay Staithe. This has been so after an Act of Parliament was passed on the 17th March 1670 which gave authority to improve the navigation of the river. It was in fact the earliest Act passed for this purpose.

Under the authority of this Act an Indenture was executed for the purpose of assessing the Lockage of the Bungay Navigation. The Indenture is dated September 7, 1672, and stipulates that for every Ton weight of Coals, Corn, Timber or other Carriage whatsoever by any Boat or Vessel, carried and conveyed between Bungay and Beccles, that shall pass through the Sass*, set down next Beccles (i.e. Geldeston), the sum of six pence and so proportionally for every greater quantity than a Ton weight, the sum of six pence. For the same weight of the same goods passing through the Sass "now set down at Ellingham Mill," the sum of twelve pence and so proportionally for every greater quantity than a Ton, but for every quantity above a hundredweight and less than a Ton weight, the sum of six pence. The rates had to be paid at the respective Sasses.* [2]

Where rivers provided facilities for water transport and the power to operate mills, there was, all too often, lengthy and heated arguments between the owners and operators of vessels and mills as to the right of water. Indeed one might say that competition for water between these particular persons was no less than rife, the River Waveney being no exception. Often such arguments resulted in litigation as related in later paragraphs.

In 1444 pandemonium broke out at Ellingham Mill when a crowd of around 500 gathered there and demolished the sluices. As the majority of these persons came from Bungay it appears that there might well have been a shortage of water in the Bungay area making navigation difficult if not impossible. One of the principal motivators and leaders of this attack was John de Martlesham of Wainford Mill, just upstream from Ellingham Mill. The result of this wanton destruction was that the stanks** ran dry, as would be expected.

Four locks were constructed within a comparatively short distance of about five miles. These were at Wainford, Ellingham, Shipmeadow and Geldeston. The original Shipmeadow Lock was situated at approximately NGR TM 373913. On William Faden's map of 1783 this lock is named "Boterys Locks" with the customary sign for a lock but there is no sign indicating that a watermill existed by or near this lock. In a document entitled "A Statement of Facts," which concerns the height of the water of the river, and published by one Jonathan Palmer, c. 1815,[3] he refers to this lock as Dan Mills' locks. On a diagram attached to this Statement two sets of locks are shown. The Shipmeadow lock is named Daniel Mills' Locks and the other as Beccles Locks. The latter would in fact be Geldeston Lock. Presumably Daniel Mills was the Lock Keeper and the fact that this particular lock was affectionately known by his name indicates he was the Keeper over many years. On a plan attached to the Auction

* Sass or Sasse — a sluice on a navigable river (Dutch).

**Stank — Scottish; a ditch, pool or tank. Old French; Estang, a pond. Latin; Stagnum, a stagnant pool.

Sale Particulars of 1884,[4] when Bungay Staithe and Navigation were offered with other properties, Shipmeadow Lock was named Mills' Locks. Beccles Lock was obviously that at Geldeston since there never has been a lock at Beccles itself. Later when this particular lock was called Geldeston Lock, it was known as such if you lived on the Norfolk side of the river otherwise if you resided on the Suffolk side it was referred to as Shipmeadow Lock.

Prior to the 1670 Act being passed the River Waveney had for some time been navigable from Yarmouth to Bungay but over the years, due to neglect, it had become obstructed and clogged up to such an extent that vessels were unable to navigate beyond Beccles. The inhabitants of the area had no alternative but to resort to land carriage in order to convey their merchandise. This form of transport was far more expensive and in turn brought about hardship and a good deal of poverty, particularly in Bungay. After the necessary improvements to the river were effected and the four locks built, trade at Bungay increased to a marked degree with a great deal of corn, flour, malt, etc., being conveyed by water to Yarmouth and other centres.

Also after the Act of 1670, Bungay Staithe and Navigation were privately owned and operated, the latter being opened in 1672. The owners were as follows:-

> 1673 Thomas Walcott;
> 1701 The Executors of Thomas Walcott;
> 1704 John Dalling and Richard Nelson (partnership dissolved in 1725);
> 1725 John Dalling who died in 1733;
> 1757 Thomas Sheriffe who died in 1768;
> 1769 Batts and Cotton;
> 1770 Henry Gooch and Thomas Cotton;
> c1775 Gooch and Barker;
> 1784 Mathias Kerrison who died in 1827;
> 1828 S. Bryant;
> 1836 Edward Butcher of Norwich, an Auctioneer*;
> post 1844 William Butcher who died in 1884;
> 1889 W.D. & A.E. Walker Limited;
> 1919 Watney, Combe, Reid & Co.[5]
> The Navigation closed in 1934.[6]

---

* Note: Although Ethel Mann states that in 1836 one Edward Butcher, of Norwich, an Auctioneer, was the owner of Bungay Staithe and Navigation, there is no mention of him under that or allied occupations, in Trade Directories of 1830 (Pigot's) and 1836 (White's). But in White's History and Gazetteer of Suffolk 1844, Edward Butcher is stated to be the Wharfinger at Bungay. *Continued on the following page.*

After the death of Thomas Sheriffe his real estate was offered for sale. This comprised a variety of properties in and around Bungay and included The Staithe and Navigation. An advertisement appeared in the local press as follows:

BUNGAY, Suffolk, June 30, 1768.

To be SOLD after one Month from the Date hereof.

THE STAITHE and NAVIGATION on the River WAVENY navigable for Keels, Lighters,* &c. from the Port of Great Yarmouth in the County of Norfolk to Bungay in the County of Suffolk, a fine trading Country, with certain Rates or Duties payable to the Owners of the faid Navigation for Carriage of Coals, Corn, Timber, and other Commodities on the faid River between the Towns of Bungay and Beccles.[7]

An undated document, but probably circa 1775, and headed "A particular of the Navigation & Estates of Messrs. Gooch and Barker in Bungay in Suffolk."[8] gives an interesting schedule of their properties and the rents received. Under the section "Description of Estates" the first is "The Staithe & Navigation on the River Waveney Navigable for Keels Lighters Wherryes and from the Port of Great Yarmouth in Norfolk to Bungay aforesaid about 30 miles through a fine trading Country with Rates and Dutyes payable to the proprietors of the said Navigation for Carriage of Coals Corn and all other Carriages on the said River between the said Towns of Bungay and Beccles (being about ten miles distant) by virtue of an Act of Parliament made in the 22 year of King Chas the 2nd (1682) the Rates or Dutyes amounting communibus annis . . . .

N.B. £100 a year has been deducted for repairs of Locks and to keep the river Navigable and £16 . . 8 . . 7 for Land Tax poor rates and other incident charges out of what appears to arise from Lockage upon an average of three years and $^3/_4$ of a year being the Time the present proprietors have enjoyed the same and which reduces the clear Annual sum arising for rates to £ a year as before set forth."

Unfortunately the two interesting amounts have been omitted. However, the occupiers of the Staithe and Navigation is given as Messrs. Gooch and

Continued from previous page

There was, however, a William Butcher of Theatre Street, Norwich who was also an Auctioneer, Land Agent and Valuer and he is listed in Trade and Street Directories of 1830, 1836, 1852 and 1854. He is again mentioned in a Norwich Street Directory of 1883 (Eyre) but his address is there given as Bank Street. It would therefore seem that Edward Butcher was in fact the owner in 1836 but at sometime after 1844 a William Butcher must have owned Bungay Staithe and Navigation because his Executors offered these and other properties for Sale by Auction in June 1884. Perhaps William was a son or brother of Edward.

* Keel — A low flat-bottomed boat
Lighter — A large open boat used in unloading and loading ships.

Barker, the Yearly Rent as £550 and the Computed Value as £5000.

Towards the end of the 18th Century it seems that the amount of goods stolen from vessels and warehouses had reached such a serious level that Notices were printed and posted as well as advertisements inserted in local papers in an attempt to prevent further losses. The Notice was as follows:-

BUNGAY NAVIGATION

WHEREAS many Frauds and Robberies have at divers times been practifed by Watermen and Others, employed upon, and living adjacent to different Parts of this Navigation. THE PROPRIETORS for the better difcovering, and preventing the like in Future, do hereby offer and promife to pay a Reward of TEN POUNDS to any Perfon who will give information of any Watermen or other Perfons, who have or may hereafter fteal, fell, conceal or embezzle in any Manner whatfoever, CORN, FLOUR, COALS, LIQUOR or MERCHANDISE from on board their Keels or Wherries, or any Craft in their employ on this Navigation, ... or off their Staithes, ... or out of their Ware houfes near the River at Bungay or Yarmouth.

And if more than one Perfon shall at any Time be concerned in fuch Frauds and Robberies, ANYONE who will give Information againft his or her Accomplice or Accomplices therein, fhall alfo be entitled to the fame Reward.

And THE PROPRIETORS

hereby farther promife, to pay a Reward of TWENTY POUNDS on Information of any Perfon or Perfons, who shall buy or receive into their Poffeffion fuch ftolen Goods as aforefaid, fo as he, fhe, or they can be lawfully convicted thereof.

This Notice is intended to be often repeated in the Norwich and Ipswich Papers; and all Offenders will be profecuted immediately, and with the utmoft Rigour of the Law.

October 3, 1780.[9]

Inspite of this publication, a wherryman, Henry Scarle, was "cruelly murdered at Whitacre Burgh" in 1787 by three men he had discovered robbing his wherry and whom he had betrayed to Matthias Kerrison, his employer. Henry Scarle is buried near the north-west corner of the vestry of Holy Trinity Church, Bungay.

After Henry Gooch and Thomas Cotton had held the Navigation and Staithe for 13 to 14 years they experienced a serious financial crisis culminating in a Commission of Bankruptcy against them. Quite why these gentlemen became bankrupt is not recorded but obviously a calamity befell them which resulted in their not inconsiderable commercial empire collapsing around them. Apart from the Staithe and Navigation they owned and occupied a residence, 4 meadows, malt-houses, a storehouse, warehouses, granaries, limekilns, stabling, a timber yard and rights of commonage. Also in their ownership were various other properties let to tenants, and these included an iron shop and warehouse, a public inn, cottages, sawhouses and pits and meadow land. In addition there were three watermills — Ditchingham, Bungay and Wainford; also a windmill at Wren's Park near the Staithe at Bungay, which formed part of their assets. Wainford Mill was held on lease from the Duke or Norfolk with pieces of land at a ground rent of £20 per annum.

The three watermills and the windmill were offered for sale by Public Auction at the Kings Head, Bungay, on Tuesday 30th March 1784.[10] A beautifully hand-written and extensive set of Particulars and Conditions of Sale gives details of all their other properties which were offered for sale by auction also at the Kings Head, Bungay, but on Tuesday 25th May 1784. It is interesting to note in these hand-written details of the properties owned by Henry Gooch and Thomas Cotton that one of the two sawhouses and pits was in the occupation of Matthias Kerrison at a yearly rent of £1.1s.0d. A new granary in Bungay which would hold upwards of 80 lasts of corn*, was also "in the occupation of Matthias Kerrison at the Yearly Rent of £11. The whole of the upper, and half the lower floors are let to him on Lease for twenty one Years, from Michaelmas 1770, at the Yearly Rent of £8 — with a covenant on the Part of the Lefsee, not to send or carry any corn or Grain from the same, during the said Term to Yarmouth or other Place down the River, except by the Wherries or other Craft of the Lefsor, his Heirs or Afsigns; and to pay him or them for the Fright thereof, the usual and customary Rates, not exceeding 6s.8d. per Last, for Wheat, Beans and Pease, and 5s. per Last for Barley, Malt and Oats; and the other half of the lower floor of the said Granary is let to the said Mr. Kerrison as Tenant at Will, at the Yearly Rent of £3." The last item in the Conditions of Sale states — "The Tavern Expenses to be paid equally by buyer and sellers."![11]

Around 1810, the income from lockage at the four locks, i.e., Wainford, Shipmeadow, Ellingham and Geldeston, was stated to be £550 and the cost of repairing wilful damage to locks in 1811 amounted to £1,085.

Matthias Kerrison then acquired the Staithe and Navigation and it would be interesting to know how he overcame the restrictive covenant regarding the

---

*A Last is a weight generally estimated at 4,000 lbs, but varying in different articles. Taking two English wheats (English white and ordinary) which average 58.13 lbs, per Imperial Bushel, then a Last (which is 80 bushels), of such corn amounts to approximately 2 tons. The granary would then have held something in the region of 160 tons. (Reference — The Roller Mill & Silo Manual by P.R. Owens, M.I.Mech. E., C.E. Third Edition, 1912.)

transport of corn or grain from the "new erected Granary" to "Yarmouth or other place down the River." It would be fair to assume he purchased the granary as well and no doubt other properties belonging to Messrs. Gooch and Cotton. Matthias Kerrison who was a renowned Bungay merchant, owned the Navigation for 43 years and he for one must be grateful to the River Waveney. During his ownership he amassed a fortune, no doubt aided by the French wars, and when he died he left property worth almost a million pounds sterling — a very considerable sum. Indeed he owned a substantial and important estate in Suffolk which was formerly the Cornwallis and Maynard estates. These he amalgamated after purchasing them in 1823.

A most intriguing hand-written document dated July 23 1785 was discovered in the Suffolk Record Office at Ipswich, the contents of which are as follows:-
"We whose name are hereunder subscribed being part owners & occupiers of the Marsh Lands in the Parishes of Mettingham, Shipmeadow, & Barsham likewise former Inhabitants, attended at the Locks called the Beccles Locks, & have given our consent to have a Water Mill erected near the said Locks, as we think it will be of real use by drawing off the water Lower than by Running over the gates . . . . A piece of 3 Inch Oak plank, 9 feet long & 10 to 11 Inches broad, was laid into the brickwork of the Mill in our presence, for Mark Water, the same height to the gates now Standing; in order that the water may not be raised higher than the said Plank, & then there can be no reason for complaint . . .

N. Burstall	
John Brown Jnr.	Jno Barnes
Robt. Draper Jnr.	John O'Brien
Simon Butcher	Simon Pitchers
William Leavold	Richd Rayner Snr.
John Reynolds	Richd Rayner Jnr.
S. Cullingford	John Fenn
Benj Garwood	John Fenn Jnr.
R. Ablett	Thos. Fenn
Jno Lincoln	Jas Howton
Tho Clay	Wm. Pitchers

These were also present at the same time the carpenters, bricklayers & Watermen . . . Many of the above have sworn to the fact, and the paper of their own signature in writing is now to be produced, being in Mr. Kerrison's possession . . . and all saw N. Lock carry the plank himself, & assisted Wm. Gibbons who spread the mortar to lay it upon, & took the level of the water with Lock . . . Names of those who have made oath to the facts, & who were then & there present . . .

Simon Pitchers	Henry Newby
Wm. Gibbons	Jonan. Palmer." [12]

There seems to be little doubt that this document refers to Geldeston or Shipmeadow Lock, and if so, then the watermill at this lock appears to have been built about 1785.

It was possibly during 1787 that Matthias Kerrison consulted his lawyers concerning an "Obstruction" to the Navigation (he acquired the Navigation in 1784). He alleged the brothers John and Lincon Machet,[a] millers at Ellingham Mill, caused it to be brought about by the lowering of the water level between Bungay and Beccles. The result of the consultation was that an action was brought by Matthias Kerrison, as plaintiff, against John and Lincon Machet, defendants. It was set down to be heard on Wednesday 25th March 1788 at the Assizes at Bury St. Edmunds before Sir Nash Grose, one of the King's Justices, and other fellow Justices. When the cause[b] came on to be tried it was ordered, by consent of the parties, that all the differences mentioned in the declaration should be referred to arbitration and the jury, who had been sworn in and impannelled, should be withdrawn. The arbitrator appointed was Thomas Maynard, Esq., of Hoxne, Suffolk, who had "agreed to take upon himself the burthen of such Arbitration."

The owner of Ellingham Mill at the time was Michael Hicks and he was invited to become a party to the reference, but he declined.

Thomas Maynard duly issued his award in writing concerning the matters in difference. After a lengthy and detailed preamble he stated, "and having thoroughly concerned the same (i.e. the differences between the parties), do ascertain, declare, award and determine, that there has not been any Obstruction to the said Navigation between Bungay in the said County of Suffolk and Beccles in the said County of Suffolk, as complained of in the said Declaration in the said Cause. And in further pursuance of the said recited Order or Rule of Reference, I do hereby direct, order and appoint as follow, (that is to say) that the Depth of three Feet five Inches of Water upon the Diamonds at Wangford Lock, upon the said Navigation, when the Water shall be level with the Surface of the Float at Ellingham Mill, shall be from henceforth deemed and taken as the Standard or Mark Water. And that the said John Machet and Lincon Machet, their Executors, Administrators and Assigns, shall from henceforth, during the Time of their interest in their said Mill, in the Time of Scarce Water, (that is to say) when the Water shall be below the Water-Mark, (and which will reduce the Depth of Water upon Wangford Diamond, to three Feet and one Inch, being the same Depth as at the Lock called Beccles Lock), have full Power and Liberty of working the Head of Water or Pen, at their said Mill, down four Inches below the middle of the Float, called Ellingham Float. And that in consideration thereof, and for the Accommodation of the

[a] Later Lincon is spelt Lincoln and the surname Matchett.
[b] A legal action between contending parties.

Navigation, the said John Machet and Lincon Machet, their Executors, Administrators, and Assigns, during the said Time, upon reasonable Notice being given to them, or either of them, or to their or either of their Servants, Agents or Workmen, that any Barge or Craft want to pass upon the said Navigation, shall, and they are hereby directed and required in all Times of such Scarce Water as aforesaid, to shut down and stop working their said Mill, from the Hour of Six o'Clock in the Morning, until the Hour of Seven o'Clock in the same morning, and from the Hour of Five o'Clock in the Afternoon, until the Hour of Six o'Clock in the same Afternoon, in order to enable such Barges and Crafts to pass upon the said Navigation. And further, that the said Matthias Kerrison shall forthwith at his own Cost and Charge, lower the Waste Gates or Floats at the Lock called the Third Lock or Dan Mills Lock, one Foot, and not suffer the Water to run or cascade over, and continue the same so lowered until they can be removed and taken away, and a wide Ware or Float can be put down in lieu thereof, of the same height as the said Waste Gates or Floats when lowered as aforesaid, and of the exact width and other dimensions as the present Float at Wangford Mill, and in the same Manner as the Float at Wangford Mill; and which said Float, I direct, order and appoint, that the said Matthias Kerrison shall forthwith at his own Cost and Charge, put the Locks, Lock-Gates, and Stakes, upon the said Navigation, into good and substantial Repair, and so from henceforth continue the same, during the Time of the interest of the said John Machet and Lincon Machet their Executors, Administrators, or Assigns in their said Mill, so that no unnecessary Waste Water shall be made or occasioned by the ill State or Condition, or want of Reparation thereof." The award also stipulated that Matthias Kerrison had to pay John and Lincon Machet the sum of £60 10s. 0d. for the costs and expenses of the Arbitration. As is usual, the award was "Signed, Sealed, published and declared by the said Arbitrator, as his final Award and Arbitration, being first duly stamped in the Presence of John Pearl and James Sewell." It was dated the 3rd November 1789.[13]

It would be fair to say justice was done to both sides in this cause but no doubt Matthias Kerrison was to some extent disappointed in the outcome inspite of the Machets having to contribute to the smooth running of the Navigation.

A Navigation Memorandum dated March 1789 reveals some interesting financial facts, including the price paid by Matthias Kerrison for the Staithe and Navigation, namely £8,000. Interest on capital sums at that time was at the rate of 5%. The details of the document are:-

"Expenses of Keeping craft and Locks in repair
12 months   400..00..00
Interest Money on £8000 being the purchase
of the Staithe & Navigation   400..00..00

About £15000 Employd. to carry on the Trade
the Interest of which amount per annum to
750..00..00
Flood Frosts and Strong Winds detain the Craft
about 10 weeks in a Year as such the Interest Money
is on 42 Weeks which amounts to £36..18 per week
No Mens Wages and Disappointments in Trade is not
valued in the above . . ." [14]

The commissioners appointed under the Act of 1670 held a meeting at the Kings Head Inn, Bungay, on April 24th 1798, the purpose of which was to ratify and confirm the order made on the 23rd November 1770 in order to "prevent as much as can or may be all Differences and Disputes whatsoever that shall or may in future arise touching or Concerning the said Navigation." The Commissioners who were present; Joseph Windham, Thomas Kerrick, Jno Smith, Thomas Jenkinson Woodward, Wolfram Lewis, John Cooper Esquires, Henry Wilson, Clerk, and John Lewis, Clerk. At the meeting they "farther ordered in consequence of a Verdict obtained by Matthias Kerrison, Merchant, the then and now proprietor of the said Navigation, At the Assizes held for the County of Norfolk, in the Year One Thousand seven hundred and ninety one, In a Cause wherein the said Matthias Kerrison was Plaintiff, and Jno. and Lincoln Matchett, Millers, the then Occupiers of the Water Mill at Ellingham next adjoining the said Navigation were Defendants tried before the Right honourable Lloyd Lord Kenyon Chief Justice of his Majesty's Court of Kings Bench, at Westminster and a Special Jury that every Wherry Boat or Vefsel lading with corn coal goods or other Merchandize pafsing through the first second third or fourth Lock or any of them should pay the whole Lockage without any exemption or abatement whatsoever."

They also resolved that the proprietors or occupiers of the water mills situated between Bungay Staithe and Beccles be ordered "not in any manner or pretence whatsoever draw or lett off the Water out of or from the said river or Navigation lower than the Ancient Water Mark of Three feet and six Inches." The idea was to prevent any "Damage or Injury" to any of the "Keels Wherrys or other Vefsels" on the River and Navigation "according to the long and established right and Usage thereof." The commissioners also laid down that persons trespassing or causing injury or damage to the Locks or the Navigation by "Drawing, letting off or running away the Water" from the River or Navigation would be liable for any damage or losses due to any keels, wherries or other vessels laden with any kind of merchandise being detained on the River for "Want of Water." Every owner or occupier of any water mill on or adjoining the River and Navigation were requested to keep up the banks and "Heddings" of the river insofar as their rights and interests extended. The same request applied to owners and occupiers of lands adjoining the River and Navigation regarding their headings of ditches, dykes and water courses "to an equal height and level with other parts of the lands adjoining thereto." In default or by refusal such owners and occupiers would, after seven days notice, be liable to pay the owner or occupier of the Navigation a sum or sums of money sufficient to rectify any injury or damage sustained.[15]

Matthias Kerrison was not disposed to allow credit for certain goods bought from his Staithe at Bungay. Perhaps it was his past experiences of uncreditworthy customers that lead him to have a notice printed which was no doubt circulated and posted in prominent places. It makes interesting reading and was as follows:-

BUNGAY STAITHE

Coals and Cinders continue to be sold at the above Staithe as ufual, for ready Money only, and the same paid for all Corn bought and delivered. — All carriages coming for coals without the Money will be returned empty, and it is hoped that none of the Cuftomers will be offended at the above regulation as to payment.

I Likewise give this Public Notice,

That I will not be anfwerable or make good to any Gentleman, Trader, or Owner of goods for damages or loffes, arifing from any accidents of the waters or of navigation, of whatever nature or kind foever (to and from Yarmouth) unlefs fuch goods are infured at the faid Staithe. — Where all goods, wares and merchandize, may be infured at one halfpenny per pound fterling, (exclufive of the Freightage) on the full amount of the value of the fame, if regularly entered and paid for, prior to their being put on board the faid Wherries, and not otherwife. For instance, if a Wherry fhould have Hogsheads of Sugar, or other articles on board, that would be deftroyed by any such accident as aforefaid, the Owner of fuch goods might think they fhould be made fatisfaction, but the trifling fum that the freight amounts to is not equivalent to the rifk; as fuch, I give this Public Notice, (to avoid any difpute), if any accident fhould happen to lofe a Pipe of Wine, or Liquor &c, in loading or unloading, or a Wherry to fink, (though fuch an accident never did happen, only in a very fmall degree of damage, yet it is poffible it may happen), that I will not be accountable for fuch accident, unlefs entered & insured as above. There are sometimes 1500L, to 2000L, worth of goods on board thefe wherries, & the freight does not amount to more than three or four pounds, it cannot be reafonable, (when the amount of the freight is not equivalent with the insurance) that the Owner of fuch Wherries or Keels fhould be accountable for accidents, without payment for fuch rifk.

M. KERRISON

Bungay, Sept, 27th, 1800.
Brightly, Printer, Bungay.[16]

From the above one obtains a glimpse of the acute business mind of Matthias Kerrison and little wonder that he amassed a fortune obviously never missing an opportunity when one was presented. Nevertheless he was a benefactor to the town of Bungay. He had the water supply brought to the town and had the Town Pump erected on the site of the old Cornmarket Cross.

The level of freight charges on the Waveney are illustrated by an extract from the accounts of William Mann, owner of both the Bungay and Wainford watermills. His accounts for February the 21st 1803 show that he sent down (presumably to Yarmouth) 100 sacks of flour by water transport at a freight charge of £1.13s.4d. plus lockage at 16s.8d. He sent down another 100 sacks of flour on March 2nd at the same charges. He also transported by water a considerable amout of barley.[17] It seems that these accounts were produced in a Court Action because at the end of the accounts is written — "Did Mr. Mann request this to be Carried at the above freight and Lockage, or did he not. Yes he did to our knowledge and many times before" (signed) S. Briant L. Irwin. The parties in dispute were Richard Mann (William's brother) and the owner of the navigation, Matthias Kerrison. In the Kings Bench a "trial" took place on the 14th March 1804 with the defendant, Richard Mann, presenting a demand for the overcharge of lockage amounting to £34.3s. In an Agreement for the Admission of Facts at the trial the amounts of lockage were stated.[18] Up to the 6th September 1803 it was 1s.0d. for every ton down to Yarmouth or up to Bungay. The Tables of Rates of Lockage were displayed at the Staithe. After the above-mentioned date the rates were 1s.6d. for every ton of heavy goods and 1s.6d. for every 40 cubic feet of light goods; 1s.0d. for every light boat or other vessel and "For every vessel passing through one Lock the same Rate of Lockage as passing through all." Information as to whether Richard Mann was successful in his "demand" has not yet been discovered.

Previously to this dispute as to the Rates of Lockage there had been a meeting of the Commissioners on the 6th September 1803 at the Kings Head Inn, Bungay, at which they discussed and settled the various rates. The result of their deliberations was set out in an instrument to which they set their "Hands and Seals." The Commissioners at that meeting were: Joseph Windham Esq., Sir Roger Kerrison, Kt., Alexander Adair, John Smith, George Stone, John James Bedingfield, Thomas Kerrich, Wolfran Lewis, John Cooper and John Cooper the younger, Esqs., and the Reverend William John Smyth and John Lewis, Clerks. In the document they stated: "that the Lockage for Coals and all heavy Goods to be paid to the Proprietors of the Navigation of the said River between Bungay and Beccles passing through the Locks thereof, was so long ago as in the Year One Thousand Six Hundred and Seventy Two, by the then Commissioners acting in Execution of the above-mentioned Act fixed at and after the rate of One Shilling and Six-pence per ton Weight; And that this Sum then assessed is now not an unfair or unreasonable Charge. We do now hereby order, direct, assess, limit and appoint the same to be paid to the said Proprietors accordingly." They also fixed the Lockage for every Wherry, Boat, or other Vessel carrying less than a ton to be one shilling. Mention also is made of the "First, Second, Third and Fourth Locks."[19] The four locks were therefore still in use in 1803. Around 80 years later, in auction Sale Particulars of Bungay Staithe and Navigation and other properties, only three locks are mentioned. The lock referred to as Daniel Mills's lock must therefore have gone out of use at sometime prior to 1884.

'Conveyance by Water' provided by the Navigation was a great boon to the tradespeople and inhabitants of the towns of Bungay, Beccles, Lowestoft and Yarmouth as well as the several nearby villages on either side of the Waveney. Wherries plied between Bungay and Yarmouth on a fairly regular basis as disclosed by directories of the 19th century:

Pigot & Co's Directory 1830
Bungay —   To Yarmouth, wherries from Bryant, Reynolds & Co.'s wharf, everyday.
Beccles —   To Bungay, wherries, every day.
To Yarmouth, wherries, twice a week from Robert Crickmore and John Crisp's wharfs.
Lowestoft—   To Yarmouth, William Albrow's wherries, from the Creek, thrice a week.

White's History & Gazetteer of Suffolk 1844
Bungay —   Wherries from the Staithe, daily to Yarmouth: Edward Butcher, Wharfinger.

Kelly's Directory of Cambridgeshire, Norfolk & Suffolk 1869
Bungay —   Wherries to Yarmouth, daily, from the Staithe, David Walker, proprietor. (He is described elsewhere in the Directory as a Corn Merchant at the Staithe, Bungay).

Kelly's Directory of Cambridgeshire, Norfok & Suffolk 1892
Bungay —   Wherries to Beccles & Lowestoft 3 times a week & to Norwich & Yarmouth when required, from the Staithe; William David & Arthur Ernest Walker, proprietors.

As in the case of other rivers, the Waveney had its share of illegal fishermen and attendant problems. In an endeavour to rectify the situation and to discourage such fishing, the following notice was published:

FISHING

Whereas great Depredations have been committed on
the River WAVENEY, by persons not authorised taking
and destroying the Fish;
Notice is hereby Given,
That any Person or Persons found Fishing for, or taking
or destroying any Fish, (not being legally authorised so
to do) with the Liberties, Rights, Royalties, Manors and
Swan Marks, of his Grace the DUKE of NORFOLK, on
the said RIVER WAVENEY, will be prosecuted according to Law, without further Notice.

By Order
John Kett,
Bailiff of the said Liberties, &c.
Bungay, May 27th 1840.

Gedge and Barker, Printers, Bury.[20]

On Monday January 19th 1818 a meeting was held at Great Yarmouth to
discuss a plan, the intention of which was to extend the Navigation as far as
Diss. After the meeting the following notice was printed and circulated:

Bungay, January 29th. 1818.
A Meeting having been held at Yarmouth on Monday, the
19th, inst. at which it was resolved to apply to Parliament
for an act to extend the Navigation of the River Waveney,
from Bungay to Diss.
Notice is hereby given, That a Meeting will be held on
Thursday the 5th day of February next, at eleven o'clock
in the forenoon at the Tuns Inn, Bungay, when and where
all persons through whose Lands the said proposed Navigation may be carried, the respective owners and occupiers of Mills upon the said River; the Inhabitants of the
Town of Bungay, and all other persons interested in the
proposed measure, are requested to attend, to take the
same into their most serious consideration
By order of
John Scott, Town Reeve of Bungay
Brightly, Printer, Bungay.[21]

A prospectus, dated January 1818, and entitled *DISS AND BUNGAY
NAVIGATION* was issued. This document extolled the several advantages of

the proposed extension. It also enumerated a considerable amount of detail, including an estimate of £36,931 to complete the undertaking which sum took account of £4,817 for contingencies. In order to obtain the likely annual tonnage, populations of Yarmouth and other towns together with "sixty-two villages within eight miles round the intended Navigation" were taken to calculate the amount of coal, corn, timber, chalk, marl, bricks, etc., required. It then stated "The probable amount of Tonnage on the line, grounded on an accurate calculation, according to the extensive population of the districts, appears to exceed 18,000 tons per annum, which, at 4d. per ton per mile, and calculating that the Craft, on an average, go about two-thirds of the line, will yield to the Company an income of about £3,975 per Annum." The intention was to form a Joint Stock Company, the shares to be £50 each; the Proprietors to have a vote in respect of each share and five shares was to be a qualification for a Directorship of the Company.[22]

Later, *Observations On The Prospectus Of The Diss And Bungay Navigation* was printed and circulated. This was a carefully compiled analysis of the proposal and it divided the Prospectus into three heads:–

"First, The estimate of the expense, . . . Second, The probable freightage to answer that expense, and . . . Third, The benefit or injury that will accrue to the proprietors and occupiers of lands in the line of the projected navigation." It was considered that "The article of bridges, calculated at £4950 is evidently extremely under-rated." Furthermore, "the whole of the sum allowed for contingencies may be added to it, and it will probably yet be insufficient," i.e., the sum of £9,767 was unlikely to cover the cost of rebuilding existing bridges and for providing others. It was also thought that "The article of compensations" was impossible "for the engineer, or any other person to judge of, in the present state of the business" and it was "therefore concluded that some thousands may be added to the general estimate of £3693." The amount of freightage likely to pass up and down the navigation was very much questioned in the observations, some sound arguments were put forward indicating that the figure of 18,000 tons per annum was somewhat optimistic.

Another matter submitted and which placed further doubt on the likely success of the project was the necessary constant supply of water. The observations stated: "It cannot be disputed, that in all lock navigations, the greater the number of vessels, which pass up and down, the greater is the supply of water required from the head and upper parts of the channel, to make up for that constant consumption. The river Waveney is subject to frequent and heavy floods in the winter, which are extremely injurious to navigation; and to a deficiency of water in the summer and autumn, to the entire stoppage of the vessels employed." It was therefore argued that a considerable amount of goods, particularly corn, would continue to be conveyed by land carriage.

An important point, naturally not mentioned in the Prospectus, was the superior advantage which the port of Ipswich possessed over that of Yarmouth. The latter was considered, for some time past, to be in a "bad state." This was because the bar at the entrance to the haven had increased so much that vessels were often delayed for a long space of time from proceeding in and out of the haven. Furthermore, "the passage to and from the sea is generally attended with great risk and hazard," occasionally with loss and damage to property. Clearly transport of goods by road to the port of Ipswich was a more attractive proposition.[23]

There was considerable local opposition to the scheme for during the proceedings a notice was printed and circulated by persons unknown. It was headed:

CAUTION
TO SUBSCRIBERS
TO THE
WAVENEY NAVIGATION

It pointed out that not one canal or navigation in fifty has been completed for the estimated sum. Furthermore it emphasised all subscribers are compelled to pay the full amount of their shares towards the work as far as it extends. It includes the opinion of "one of the first engineers in the kingdom" that double the estimate would not complete the present plan. In the event of the navigation extending only to Harleston at the cost of £36,000, a question is asked, "will the good people of that town who are now so eager for the measure, come forward with additional subscriptions, or will they not rather retain to themselves the advantages which they expect from the credulity of their neighbours?" The publication finally says that Yarmouth "cares not which is injured," i.e. Harleston or Diss, but the latter will be too late to benefit when its trade is transferred to its more fortunate rival Harleston.[24]

Active opposition to the proposals crystallised in a committee formed to oppose the petition for its furtherance. This committee met in Bungay on the 17th February 1818 and, having learned that a petition was, on Friday 13th instant, presented to the House of Commons for extending the Navigation from Bungay to Diss, it resolved "that books should be opened to receive subscriptions to defray the expenses of opposing the same, . . ." The committee then sent a printed copy of the resolution to every person interested in opposing the measure. The chairman of the meeting was Mr. J.J. Bedingfield.

Another notice, printed by Mr. G. Woodfall of Angel Court, Skinner Street, London, was issued which also strongly objected to the extension of the navigation. The notice pointed out that the projected extension was "a mere speculation of a few trading persons in Yarmouth." It further stated that the measure was "highly injurious to the Rights, Interests and Comforts, as well as contrary to the wishes of the great majority of the Owners and Occupiers on the Line, to most of the Proprietors of the Mills, and against the consent of the Possessors of the present Navigation to Bungay . . ." In the hope that weight would be added against the proposition, the following eminent persons were stated to be opposers;

"Lord Maynard, the Bishop of Salisbury, Lord George Beresford, Sir William Dalling, Mr. Irby, Mr. Adair, Sir E. Kerrison, Mr. Kerrison, Mr. Bedingfield, Mr. Woodward, Mr. Smith and many other Gentlemen of the Greatest respectability in that neighbourhood, whose intention it is to present a Petition against it."[25]

However, after all the deliberations and campaigning for and against the navigation extension, its termination remained as before at Bungay Staithe.

It will be remembered that William Butcher probably acquired Bungay Staithe and Navigation sometime after 1844. He was a Norwich auctioneer and died during the early part of 1884. The executors of his will, who were also the mortgagees of his estate, arranged a sale by Auction of all his properties. This was held at the Kings Head Hotel, Bungay on Thursday June 19th 1884 and conducted by Messrs. Spelman of Norwich and Yarmouth. The estate was to be offered in its entirety and if not so sold then in seven lots. Lot 1 was described as the "Commodious Mercantile Premises & Staithe at Bungay and the Bungay and Beccles Navigation. Where an extensive Trade has been carried on for upward of a century." It included a double-roofed granary with shoots into boat dyke, cake and salt house, malt-house, 75-coombe steep with three floors, malt store, kiln and furnace house, opening into boat dyke; large coal warehouse paved with Yorkshire stone, lime kiln, and chalk-house; also the dyke on the south side. Range of coal-houses, blacksmith's shop, yard, staithe, and wherry slip. The timber yard and long staithe next the Mill Dyke. Also a granary and cake-house in the occupation of Messrs. Walker at the annual rent of £10; the whole containing about 4a.3r.1p. This was divided as follows:-

Nos on Plan	Description	A.	R.	P.
		Quantity		
2	Timber Yard	1	0	15
3	Coal Yard	0	2	34
Part 8	Granaries, Yard, &c.	0	2	0
10	Mill Stream	0	1	26
11	Coal Yard Cut	0	1	23
12	Lime Kiln Cut	0	1	20
13	Land at Ellingham Lock	0	1	12
14	" " Mills' Lock	0	0	30
17	" " Ellingham Lock	0	1	24
19	Lock Cut	0	1	17
		4	3	1

[Note: No. 14 on the plan is named, "Site of Late Mills' Lock Pt. Lot 1."]

Also included in this lot were the dues or tolls authorised to be collected on the Navigation, and the Wainford, Ellingham and Shipmeadow Locks constructed therein. The tolls are paid on coals, corn, timber or other articles or goods passing through the Locks. From 1875 to 1882 they averaged nearly 8000 tons per annum. The authorised tolls to be charged were as follows:-

"For every Ton of Goods by any Vessel carried between Bungay and Beccles passing through the Lock next Beccles, the sum of sixpence $(2^1/_2p)$, and so on proportionally for every greater quantity than a Ton; and for every Vessel having in it above a Hundredweight and less than a Ton of Goods or Passengers carried between Beccles and Bungay that shall pass through the said Lock the sum of sixpence.

And for every ton of Goods by any Vessel carried between Bungay and Beccles, passing through the Lock at Ellingham Mill, The sum of One Shilling (5p.), and so on proportionally for every greater quantity than a Ton; and for every Vessel having in it above a Hundredweight and less than a Ton of Goods or Passengers between Beccles and Bungay, passing through the Lock at Ellingham Mill, the sum of sixpence. All the above Rates to be taken at Shipmeadow Lock next Beccles."

Lot 2 was a malting, range of granaries, large yard, wherry cut and staithe; also a cottage and garden let at an annual rent of £5. Lot 3 A small piece of meadow land of 1a.1r.6p. Lot 4 meadow land of 5a.0r.10p. Lot 5 dwelling-house and garden, various outbuildings, mill house, malt chamber and granary, in all 1a.1r.26p. Lot 6 a stable let at £1 per annum. Lot 7 at Geldeston Lock a free public house and land called The Lock House, in all 3a.3r.5p. [26] The tenant of Lot 7 was Alexander Gordon. He was a yearly tenant of part of the land at £4 per annum and the public house he held rent free as part of his wages for attending to the Locks and Navigation.

Although, as mentioned above, W.D. & A.E. Walker Ltd. are stated as being the owners of the Staithe and Navigation in 1889, it is thought they probably purchased them at auction in 1884. They were the well-known Bungay Millers, Maltsters and Merchants who also owned a fleet of wherries some of which were built at the Staithe at Bungay.[27] Their fleet included the famous "Albion" which was launched from William Brighton's Yard at Lake Lothing c. 1898 and is now restored and run by the Norfolk Wherry Trust.[28]

The last owners of the Staithe and Navigation were Messrs. Watney, Combe Reid & Co., acquiring them in 1919.

Apart from providing navigation facilities as far as Bungay, the river powered several watermills, some of which were in existence before the Domesday Survey of 1080–1086. It also produced many hundredweights of eels which was a useful and lucrative perk to the millers.

The Waveney is fed by various tributaries, including the River Dove which joins it at Hoxne; with these and the fact that upland field drainage has been vastly improved of late, the river is given to flooding easily in times of heavy and continuous rain. Two notable floods occurred in August 1912 (usually referred to as The Great Flood), and August 1968 when the waters rose to great heights and caused considerable damage and inconvenience. Even in the winter of 1987/88 the marshes adjoining the Waveney were virtually completely flooded, and to some distance from the river itself, such flooding being due in no small measure to the very wet summer of 1987. Flooding is in no way a modern phenomenon. A disaster struck in 1609, when the Waveney Valley was one of several which flooded as a result of coastal dunes and defences being breached by the sea. Shortly afterwards an Act was passed "for the speedye Recoverye of manye thousand Acres of Marsh Groundes . . . . latelye surrounded by the Rage of the Sea." [29]

John Barber Scott records in his diary for August 15th 1828, "Water has risen in the Waveney 4 to $4\,{}^1/_2$ feet since yesterday morning. It crosses the Earsham Dam & comes over the gravel walk in my garden." (Waveney House, Bungay.) From other entries in his diary one deduces there had been incessant rain from 4th July 1828 for 47 days.

The flowing water of the Waveney is unfortunately no longer used to power mills but it provides a great deal of pleasure insofar that fishing is much enjoyed along its banks and on its lower reaches a great deal of sailing and boating takes place.

As B. Granville Baker in "Waveney" 1924 so aptly puts it:

"What though Bartholomew's map marks this river's course with an emphatically dotted line, I hope to have proved that the boundary which Waveney represents is purely an inter-county, an administrative matter, and that, Waveney's duties as frontier are those becoming to a stream of venerable age and great respectability, are in fact reward and honour to a well-conducted and popular servant to the public."

In November 1990, it was announced that maintenance work on long disused locks on a stretch of the River Waveney was to be carried out in case navigation on it is re-opened.

Earlier in the year a local group promoted the idea by raising a petition to test the feeling of residents on the idea of re-opening the navigation between Geldeston and Bungay. It was believed such a move would boost business in Bungay and enhance the town as a venue for holidaymakers.

The petition contained several hundred signatures and was presented to the Broads Authority together with the aims of the concept. A copy of the petition was also forwarded to the National Rivers Authority.

There was a strong opposition to the proposal organised by a member of the Bungay Cherry Tree Angling Club. It was claimed the counter-petition attracted no less than 4,000 signatures.[30]

Recent changes of considerable concern have been brought about to the River Waveney. A borehole was sunk near the source of the river and large quantities of water are frequently abstracted resulting in the lowering of the water table and the drying out of Redgrave and Lopham Fens. The source of the Waveney has also dried out and all that one now sees is a wadi. Indeed the springs that fed both the Waveney and the Little Ouse, which runs west, have now been dry for many years.

Another aggravation affecting the river is pollution which is mainly from agricultural concerns. Although not a major problem on Redgrave and Lopham Fens, or the headwaters, it is a consideration further downstream.

It is to be hoped that satisfactory solutions to these difficulties will be found and implemented in the not too distant future.

THE RIVER WAVENEY AND ITS NAVIGATION

S.R.O. (I) — Suffolk Record Office, Ipswich
S.R.O. (L) — Suffolk Record Office, Lowestoft
N.R.O. — Norwich Record Office

1. The Revd. George Munford, "An Attempt to Ascertain The True Derivation of The Names of Towns And Villages, And of Rivers, And Other Great Natural Features in the County of Norfolk," 1870.
2. S.R.O. (L) Acc. 187/1. Collection of MSS and Notes for Ethel Mann's book,"Old Bungay".
3. S.R.O. (I) HA85/3116/630
4. Messrs. Spelman, Norwich and Yarmouth, auction Sale Particulars 1884; original copy in Bungay Museum.
5. Ethel Mann, "Old Bungay", 1934, p.148, amended by Author.
6. Robert Maltster, "Wherries and Waterways", 1971, p.23.
7. From an unknown local newspaper, probably The Journal, published in Lowestoft. Kindly supplied by Dr. Hugh Cane.
8. Original document in Bungay Museum.
9. S.R.O. (I) HA85/3116/586.
10. Ipswich Journal 27th March 1784.
11. Original document in Bungay Museum.

12.   S.R.O. (I) HA85/3116/657.
13.   S.R.O. (L) Acc. 187/1, Op. Cit.
14.   S.R.O. (I) HA85/3116/22.
15.   S.R.O. (I) HA85/3116/24.
16.   S.R.O. (I) HA85/3116/649.
17.   S.R.O. (I) HA85/3116/23 & 31.
18.   S.R.O. (I) HA85/3116/21.
19.   S.R.O. (I) HA85/3116/590.
20.   S.R.O. (L) Acc. 187/1, Op. Cit.
21.   S.R.O. (L) Acc. 187/1, Op. Cit.
22.   Copy of document in Bungay Museum.
23.   Copy of document in Bungay Museum.
24.   S.R.O. (I) HA85/3116/629.
25.   S.R.O. (L) Acc. 187/1, Op. Cit.
26.   Messrs. Spelman, Op. Cit.
27.   Robert Maltster, Op. Cit.
28.   Julia Carter, "Gift Scheme for 'grand old lady'" Eastern Daily Press, 9th September 1988.
29.   David Dymonds, "The Norfolk Landscape," 1985, p.208.
30.   Eastern Daily Press, 12th November, 1990.

The Flax Mill, Scole, Norfolk

NGR TM139790

This was the first mill on the banks of the River Waveney going downstream from its source. It stood on the Norfolk side some 1 $^1/_2$ miles east of Diss and a $^1/_2$ mile or so west of Scole with some of its buildings fronting Waterloo Lane.

The River Waveney provided ample facilities for retting flax (i.e. soaking it in water) which is the process of preparing the flax for use by rotting the useless part of the plant through fermentation. Flax had long been grown in the area as the following extract shows:-

James Read, farmer of Hoxne, produced 149 stone of flax from 3 acres in 1787 and 174 stone grown on 4 acres in 1788. He was the farmer who grew the largest amounts and was one of 15 claimants for the bounty for growing hemp and flax in 1799 in the Eye and Hoxne districts.[1]

The Flax Mill was not a watermill but one that was powered by steam. One can attribute its inception to the acute poverty and unemployment prevalent in rural districts in the mid-1840's; the latter being brought about by a series of depressions in agriculture consequent upon the defeat of Napoleon at Waterloo and the cessation of hostilities with France. During this period Charles Fisher Costerton of Eye, Suffolk, was Clerk and later Registrar and Auditor to the Hartismere Union. His appointment brought him into all too frequent contact with the extreme poverty prevailing in the rural districts.[2] This experience caused C.F. Costerton to give considerable thought to the problem of the prevailing unemployment and consequent poverty.

In order to reduce agricultural insolvencies and so minimise resulting unemployment amongst farmworkers, C.F. Costerton persuaded farmers to grow flax (Linum usitatissimum). Indeed he conducted an enthusiastic campaign among farmers emphasising the value of flax for its fibres and the oil containing seed (linseed oil). The flax fibres were used to produce linen sheeting, shirting, sacking, twine and rope. His campaign was obviously successful and he can aptly be described as a modest 19th century philanthropist.

In 1854 C.F. Costerton built the flax mill beside the Waveney [3] and its tall brick built chimney was a noted landmark in the district. The mill was quite extensive. According to the Ordnance Survey 25 inch map of 1886, the main building measured about 245 feet by 50 feet with other sections adjoining providing further large floor areas. Perhaps the buildings might more appropriately be designated a factory as no doubt some industrial archaeologists would feel such a nomenclature more fitting.

C.F. Costerton had his brother-in-law Peter Naylor as his partner in the business and they had a processing factory at Eye in Suffolk, also built in 1854, which was run in conjunction with the Scole Mill.

In order to encourage flax growing the partnership instituted the "Costerton and Naylor" Cup which was awarded for the best three acres of flax in the district. It was presented at an annual dinner held at Eye.[4] However in the 1860's an outbreak of Rinderpest caused vast numbers of cattle to die or to be slaughtered. As a result of this calamity the demand for root crops diminished and so flax was substituted as a crop by even more farmers in an effort to maintain some kind of income.[5]

The Flax Mill continued successfully but only for a comparatively short period. In 1862 Costerton and Naylor were awarded the Prize Medal at the International Exhibition and around that time they employed about one hundred people at both Scole and Eye.[6] Many of the workers were Irishmen who were used to working with flax. Once a week the machines and boilers were slackened so that necessary cleaning operations could be carried out. This was done by a Mr. John Woodcock who was the village blacksmith.[7] He owned the village forge and worked there up to 1914 when he died at the age of 79.[8]

In common with other mills, the Flax Mill suffered severe outbreaks of fire — no less than five but somehow managed to survive on each occasion. The most serious was in 1871 which resulted in almost total destruction. It was thought that these fires were started by sparks produced by grit coming into contact with the spikes of the scutchers[9] (machines which bruised the stems and broke the woody part so that the fibres were separated). A fire in 1864 completely destroyed the factory at Eye.

Eventually, for a variety of reasons, the supply of flax from farmers declined and, with competition from overseas, the Flax Mill's production suffered and soon came to a halt. After an effort to revive the business under the name of The British Flax & Paper Co., which proved very much a temporary expedient, the Flax Mill closed down in 1881.[10] Soon afterwards the machinery was removed and demolition of the buildings took place and so, after merely 27 years, this enterprise came to an end. All that remains of Scole Flax Mill are an extremely small section of the buildings (probably used as stabling originally) and a house recently renovated and known as Flax Farm Craft Centre.

In Harrod's Trade Directory of 1863, Naylor & Costerton are described as

"Flax Manufacturers" whereas in Harrod's Directory of 1872, C.F. Costerton is credited as being a "Flax Spinner and Manufacturer". Kelly's Directories of 1875 and 1877 each give C.F. Costerton as "Flax Manufacturer".

After the Flax Mill closed down Charles Fisher Costerton continued to live at Scole House where he died in 1891 aged 67.[11]

THE FLAX MILL, SCOLE

1. Nesta Evans, "The East Anglian Linen Industry, Rural Industry and Local Economy", 1985, p.118.
2. Eric Pursehouse, "Waveney Valley Studies", Reprinted 1983, p.193.
3. Ibid. p.193.
4. Ibid. p.194.
5. Ibid p.194.
6. Ibid p.193.
7. J. Mallows, "Scole from Past to Present, The Flaxmill Scole", undated publication, but post 1959, pp.20 and 21.
8. Ibid. p.11.
9. Eric Pursehouse, Op. Cit. p.194.
10. Eric Pursehouse, Op. Cit. p. 195.
11. Eric Pursehouse, Op. Cit. p.195.

Hoxne Watermill, 1988. Robert Jackson.

Hoxne Watermill, 1988. Part of the first floor showing two pairs of stones enclosed by vats, crown wheel, layshaft and pulleys. Robert Jackson.

Hoxne Watermill, Suffolk

NGR TM189778

Proceeding downstream this is the first watermill on the Waveney. The Domesday Survey states that at "Hoxana", "then as now 2 mills." It is therefore possible that the present site is an ancient one although one cannot be certain where the two Domesday mills stood in "Hoxana", i.e. the two pairs of stones. The present mill stands on the Suffolk side of the river about $^3/_4$ mile below the village and at the end of a single track lane. It was built in 1846 as a textile mill, later converted to a corn mill, and replaced an earlier mill which is said to have been erected in 1749.[1] A stone in the garden of the mill house is inscribed $^{TP}_{1749}$ and it was this that was taken to date the predecessor of the present structure. The brickwork on the west corner of the present mill has been inscribed as follows:-

PRIMUS LAPIS HUJUS
MOLAE AQUATILIS
POSTUS EST 29 DIE AUGUS
MDCCCXLVI

LIEU [T]	GEN[L]
SIR E	KERRISON
BART	MP

Keith Falconer in his book "Guide to England's Industrial Heritage" indicates that the present mill was built in 1747 as a flax factory and later converted to corn milling. But Rex Wailes in his paper entitled "Suffolk Watermills" read at the Newcomen Society's Meeting at the Science Museum on 7th April 1965, states Hoxne Mill replaces an earlier mill of 1749 which had been converted from corn to a textile mill. The two statements do not tie up but clearly, in the light of site evidence, the information provided by Rex Wailes is correct. However in White's Directory of Suffolk 1844, mention is made that the corn mill had recently been converted into a flax and linen manufactory. This indicates the earlier mill was converted somewhat later in its life.

Hoxne Mill is a fine, reasonably well preserved example and typical of the smaller East Anglian boarded watermills. It is three storeyed and built of brick up to the first-floor level, thereafter it is timber-framed and weatherboarded under a gabled and slate covered roof. The lucam, (from the French "lucarne" meaning a dormer window), has pleasing curved supporting brackets and at one time the mill had a weather vane. At the rear is a red-bricked extension with a steam engine house and the usual tall brick chimney stack. The present mill was equipped with 4 pairs of stones (2 pairs in 1968), and an iron undershot wheel 15ft. 9ins. diameter by 6ft. 8 ins. wide made by Knights of Harleston who were the millwrights generally associated with this mill. Primary drive gear ratio is 172:39. It has a split pitwheel and the wallower could be raised out of gear by operating two screws. The iron upright shaft ranges from 6ins. diameter at the wallower to 15 ins. diameter at the Great Spur Wheel. It has mortise Wheels and its Great Spur Wheel was split. The mill is fitted with Governors, a grind stone, a crane (for raising and lowering the upper or runner stone for dressing purposes), and a Tattershall's midget $^{1}/_{2}$ sack roller plant. It was also equipped with a semi-portable steam plant by Youngs of Diss but it is not known when this was first employed.[2] The late John Munnings (grandson of John Munnings of Mendham Mill and nephew of Sir Alfred Munnings), stated that the $^{1}/_{2}$ sack roller plant "was always in trouble."[3] Quite what he meant by this statement is not related but presumably it did not run smoothly and it may have broken down from time to time.

Hoxne Mill is shown on the following early maps:-

Kirby's (Suffolk) 1736, Bowen's (Suffolk) 1760, Faden's (Suffolk) 1783, Faden's (Norfolk) 1797, A. Bryant's 1824/5 and 1826 and on this latter map it is named "Stone Mill." Also on the first edition of the 1 inch Ordnance Survey Map 1837, the mill is designated "Flax Mill." On the 1904 edition of the 25 inch Ordnance Survey Map it is shown as a "Corn Mill." It is curious that this mill was called "Stone Mill" at one time. The reason appears somewhat obscure — unless it is all too obvious!

By 1769 William Clarke had occupied the earlier Hoxne watermill, and probably did so some years previously, because it is recorded that his second son, Thomas Clarke, was born at Hoxne. Thomas learnt the craft of milling at his father's mill and at the age of 24 he took over Earsham Watermill in 1793. William Clarke was quite a character and was a well-known figure on the Norfolk and Suffolk corn markets. He also possessed considerable strength since he was reputed to be able to lift, from the floor, two sacks of corn, one under each arm and each weighing 280lbs.! Apart from being a miller, William Clarke was also a farmer and a baker. It is also of interest to note that William Clarke supplied the square post for Hoxne windmill from a tree on his farm, the post measured 10ft. 5ins. in circumference, and he actually built the windmill.[4]

In 1784 the miller was William Cook and on the 16th of November of that year he insured his "dwelling house brick and tiled" for £150, his "Water Corn Mill and going gears belonging, timber and tiled" for £300 and "Utensils and Stock therein" for £200.[5]

John Roper, in 1816, occupied the mill as tenant, it being copyhold of the Manor of Hoxne Hall with the Priory. In December of that year the mill with a dwelling house, stables, etc., was offered for sale by auction, subject to John Roper's lease of which eleven years were unexpired from Michaelmas last.[6] It is not known whether a sale was effected. But some fifteen years later John Roper appears to have run into financial difficulties. On the 14th September 1831 he executed an indenture whereby he assigned all his estate for the benefit of his creditors.[7] Then in 1836 a fiat in bankruptcy was made against "John Roper the Elder, late of Hoxne and Syleham in the County of Suffolk, Miller and flour merchant." He was ordered to surrender on the 26th September 1836 at the Kings Head Inn, Beccles.[8] It is thought that Syleham mentioned in this bankruptcy notice refers to the windmill in the village and not the watermill.

By 1840 Henry Warne had occupied Hoxne mill and in common with others operating similar concerns he employed children as well as adults. A pitiful and tragic event connected with the mill was reported at the end of January 1840. Two small factory girls aged 9 and 11 were drowned in the River Waveney as they were returning home from the watermill.[9]

A new 8 year lease was granted to Henry Warne in 1841 by Sir Edward Kerrison of Oakley Park, Suffolk, who is described in the lease as the "owner or proprietor of a certain dwellinghouse Water Mill Steam Engine Machinery and Buildings with appurtenances situated and being in Hoxne." The yearly rental of £125 was payable from the seventh day of October 1840.[10] In the Lease, the mill is described as having an undershot water wheel, pit wheel, bevelled nut on an upright shaft and an upright shaft with a large crown wheel. Henry Warne is shown as a "Manufacturer" which implies that he worked as a linen manufacturer at the time and therefore used Hoxne mill for textile purposes as opposed to corn milling. Indeed the Lease makes no mention of mill stones or dressing machinery.

Fourteen years later, in July 1855, the "dwellinghouse Watermill Steam Engine lands and premises at Hoxne Suffolk and Thorpe Abbots Norfolk" were leased for a term of eleven years but at a distinctly lower rent, namely £70 per annum, notwithstanding "lands" at Hoxne and Thorpe Abbotts were on this occasion included. The lessor was Sir Edward Clarence Kerrison and the lessees Messrs. George Godbold (farmer) and George Chase (miller) both of Metfield, Suffolk. The Lease recites, inter alia, ". . . it is expressly declared and agreed between the said parties — it shall be lawful for the said Sir Edward Clarence Kerrison his heirs and assigns at all times during this demise to use and exercise the full and absolute power and authority and control over the river or stream and supply of water to the said watermill by lowering raising or widening the float which regulates such supply at his or their discretion. . ."[11] This reservation seems to be an unreasonable imposition and one that could cause difficulty and produce problems for the miller. Quite why the lessor retained control in this manner is difficult to understand. Surely it was in his best interest that the mill should function without disturbance but maybe the inclusion of the reservation was counterbalanced by the apparent modest rent.

The second and third schedules of the lease are very descriptive and explicit insofar as the machinery and fixtures in and about the mill are concerned. So much so they would be more than useful in reinstating the mill in the event of a calamity befalling the structure. The two schedules are produced at Appendix A.

The operators of this mill gleaned from various trade directories, etc. are:-

1844	Thomas Coleby, linen manufacturer and spinner [12]
1844–1846	Henry Sharman, corn miller[13]
1855 & 1865	Daniel Boyles, miller[14]
1855–1892	John Chase, corn miller[15]
1855	James C. Seaman, corn miller[16]
1868	Horace Bacon, miller[17]

(it is likely that some of the above-named were wind millers and not at Hoxne Watermill but the Directories do not differentiate).

1873	George Rayner, miller[18]
1879	George Rayner, jnr., miller and shopkeeper[19]
1897	E.C. Pike

On the 24th June 1892 John Chase died at his residence in Hoxne. He had operated Hoxne Watermill for some 37 years and from around 1883 he had taken his two sons into partnership carrying on business at both Hoxne and Diss.[20]

In July 1897 part of Dame Mary Kerrison's Trust Estate was submitted to public auction. The Estate comprised 121 lots and included 10 fully-licensed public houses and Beerhouses, 16 Farms with Homesteads, totalling about 1747 acres 0 roods 26 perches, meadow, accommodation and allotment land, private residences, 80 small houses, cottages and smith's shops in Suffolk and Norfolk. The properties were offered for sale by Messrs. Stafford and Rogers, Auctioneers, 83 High Street, Bedford at the Town Hall, Eye, Suffolk on Tuesday and Wednesday 13 & 14 July 1897 at 2 p.m. each day.

Lot 70 of this Estate included the Hoxne Watermill and the particulars were as follows:-

The Highly Valuable Property
situate in the Parish of Hoxne, Suffolk, and Thorpe Abbots,
Norfolk, and consisting of
A Substantially Brick-Built and Slated
Residence known as Waveney House
which contains Hall and 2 Reception Rooms, Kitchen and Scullery,
Dairy, Pantry, 5 Bedrooms, and Box Room, also Cottage
adjoining containing 4 rooms, Wood-barn, Coal-House,
and 2 W.C.'s, together with
THE THREE STOREY MILL
and Premises with Water wheel and 2 Main wheels, Boiler
house, Engine room, Office, 2 Bay Cart-shed, 3 Bay Open
shed, Lean-to Open shed, Gig house, Calves' place,
stabling for 4 horses with Granary over, and 4 bay open
shed, and Cow-house, &c., also
FIVE ENCLOSURES OF VALUABLE MEADOW LAND
The Whole Comprising
12A.   OR.   17P.
No. 650 is let (with other property) to Mr. J.R. Neeve at an
entire rent of £389 2s. 0d., of which £2 15s. 0d. is
apportioned to this Lot. The remainder is let to Mr. E.C. Pike
at a rent of £15 0s. 0d.

SCHEDULE

No. on Ordnance	Parish	Description	Culture	Name of Tenant	Acreage A. R. P.	Rental
637	Hoxne	Mill & Premises		E.C.Pike	0 2 28	
651	"	Waveney House & Gardens		"	0 2 15	
217	Thorpe Abbots	Long Meadow	Pasture	"	2 0 24	
239	"	Meadow	"	"	1 3 16	
240	"	"	"	"	1 0 15	
241	"	"	"	"	2 3 37	
					9 1 15	£15 0s 0d
650	Hoxne			J.R. Neeve	2 3 2	£2 15s 0d
					A12 0 17	£17 15s 0d

With this Lot are sold the water rights attaching to the Mill,
but such water rights are subject to an Agreement with
Geo. Holt Wilson, Esq., dated 1st June, 1885, under which
the control of such rights is vested in Mr. Wilson in
consideration of a payment of £15 per annum. This Agreement
will determine on the 6th April, 1898, and in the
meantime the purchaser will be entitled to the benefit of
such Agreement, including an apportioned part of the
rent of £15 under the said Agreement.[21]

John Chase, junior, purchased at auction Hoxne mill with the house, etc., on
the 14th July 1897 (the second day of the sale) and paid £500.[22]

Further relevant dates are as follows:-

1900/08   Chase Brothers (steam, wind and water) and at Diss.[23]

1916/22   Chase Brothers, Victoria Road, Diss and at Hoxne (steam, wind
            and water).[24]

1920's   George Bridges, miller, lived in the cottage behind the mill house,
            the latter was occupied by Mr. Chase who owned the mill. Like
            others,George Bridges caught a great many eels with nets and they
            were regularly sent to Billingsgate. He also hired out rowing boats
            for Mr. Chase.[25]

1920–21   Chase Brothers, koh-i-nor Roller Mills, Diss, and Hoxne.[26]

1929   Alfred Dyball, Farmer, Low Farm and miller, steam and water.[27]
            At Michaelmas of this year Alfred Dyball sold the mill, the mill
            house, cottage, farm buildings, the farmhouse, a fine old barn
            and about 50 acres to Leonard Walker R.I., artist. His son,
            Renton Walker, ran the mill and farm. The purchase price was
            approximately £1500. Corn was taken in from neighbouring farmers
            for grinding for which they paid about six pence ($2^1/_2$p) per
            coomb.[28]
            (Rex Wailes states the mill was closed down in 1928 but clearly
            this is incorrect).

1931   Mill and Farm sold by Mr.L. Walker for just over £2000.[29]

1965   Mill used as a factory.[30]

1968   The mill and house and about 10 acres were offered for sale by
            auction on Friday 14th June by Thomas William Gaze of Diss and
            Jackson-Stops and Staff of Newmarket and London W.1. but did
            not sell. It was then offered for sale by private treaty at an asking
            price of £13,500. It eventually sold and is privately owned.

When Leonard Walker owned the mill and farm he converted the barn to a Studio
where he held art classes.[31] The Barn still stands but is now used as a store.

It is interesting to note that at one time two Postmills, one of the open trestle type, and the other with a roundhouse, stood only 200 yards to the south-east of the Watermill and at a level of some 50ft. higher. One appears on a map of 1783 and 1824, the other on a map of 1826 but was demolished in 1923. This latter windmill was known as Chase's Mill. The other was known as Cross Street Mill.[32] It will be seen from the above notes on millers that a John Chase and Daniel Boyles were millers at Hoxne in 1855-65. It is uncertain as to whether they were both wind and/or watermillers at that time. In 1892 John Chase was still a miller in the village but by the turn of the century, Chase Brothers were steam, wind and water millers at Hoxne and carrying on business at Diss at the same time. This implies that they owned and/or occupied both the watermill and one or both of the windmills at Hoxne.

The waterwheel is in situ and, it is understood, quite an amount of machinery still remains in the mill but unfortunately the writer was unable to obtain permission from the owners to inspect the interior.

Hoxne Watermill and the Mill House are both Listed Buildings Grade II under the Town & Country Planning Acts. Furthermore, they are privately owned and the Mill is not open to the public.

HOXNE WATERMILL

1. Rex Wailes, "Suffolk Watermills", Excerpts Transactions of the Newcomen Society, 1964–1965, p.p. 106, 107, 110.
2. Ibid. p.p. 102, 103, 104, 105, 106, 107.
3. John Munnings, "The Passing of the Country Miller and his Mill, Rivers Stour and Waveney," unpublished article, c. 1970.
4. "The Miller", October 2nd 1893.
5. Sun Fire Insurance Policy No. 498524 (Vol. 324).
6. Ipswich Journal, November 9th 1816.
7. London Gazette, 30th September 1831.
8. London Gazette, 16th August 1836.
9. Suffolk Chronicle, 1st February 1840.
10. S.R.O. (I) HA/68/2593/1238.
11. S.R.O. (I) HA/68/484/673.
12. White's Directory.
13. Kelly's Directories, 1844 & 1845 & Post Office Directory 1846.
14. White's Directory, 1855 & Kelly's Directory 1865.
15. White's Directory, 1855, Post Office Directory 1858, Harrod's Directory 1864, Morris' Directory 1868, Post Office Directory 1869, Harrod's Directory 1873, White's Directory 1874, Kelly's Directory 1883 and White's Directories 1891 and 1892.

16.   White's Directory 1855.
17.   Morris' Directory 1868.
18.   Harrod's Suffolk & Cambs. Directory 1873.
19.   Kelly's Directory of Suffolk & Norfolk 1879.
20.   "The Miller", July 4th 1892.
21.   S.R.O. (I) fsc 152/1.
22.   "The Miller", August 2nd 1897.
23.   Kelly's Directories, 1900 and 1908.
24.   Ibid. 1916, 1920 and 1922.
25.   J.J. Maling, "The Miller of Hoxne", Eastern Daily Press 4th May 1974.
26.   Eastern Counties of England Trades Directory 1920–1921.
27.   Kelly's Directory 1929.
28.   Renton Walker Esq., Wells-next-the Sea.
29.   Ibid.
30.   Rex Wailes, Op. Cit.
31.   Renton Walker Esq., Op. Cit.
32.   Brian Flint, "Suffolk Windmills", 1979, p.135.

Syleham Watermill, Suffolk

NGR TM 213792

It is quite likely that this is a Domesday Mill site, the mill at that time being owned by the monks of the Monastery situated south of the town of Thetford and founded in 1020. The Domesday Survey states at "Seilanda — And 1 mill."

Herbert de Losinga (or Losing), 1st Bishop of Norwich (d.1119), gave to Roger Bigot, or rather to the Cluniac Priory of Thetford, then lately founded by him, a manor, and the Church of Syleham, being his own private property, with all that belonged to them, as the watermill, fishery, etc. in exchange for Tombland, and other possessions settled by Roger on the Cathedral of Norwich.[1]

This mill was situated on the Suffolk side of the river in the parish of Syleham, about $^1/_4$ mile south of the village of Brockdish and the A143 road. The mill appears on the early maps of 1736 (Kirby's), 1760 (Bowen's), 1783 (Faden's), 1797 (Faden's) and 1824–6 (Bryant's) when it would then have been a corn mill but in 1839 a large portion of it was converted to a weaving mill,[2] the looms being operated by water power.

In 1779 William Mann of Syleham, "Miller, Corn Merchant and Farrier," insured his "dwellinghouse situated aforesaid (Syleham) brick Pannelled and tiled" for £400; his "Water Corn Mill with the going gears therein brick and tiled" for £800; "Utensils and stock therein" for £700. The watermill was stated to be situated at Syleham. William Mann also insured Weybread Water Corn Mill and the utensils and stock at the same time. It therefore appears he owned and was operating both mills in 1779.[3]

The last watermill at Syleham was built with timber framing, weatherboarded exterior and a tiled roof. It is therefore interesting to note that in the insurance policy of 1779, the mill is described as brick and tiled. If this is correct, it is likely that this earlier mill was a comparatively small affair which was, in due course, replaced by the large timber built and tiled mill which was eventually completely destroyed by fire. (See below).

The last mill was a three-storeyed building of timber frame construction on a brick base and clad with white painted weatherboarding under a gabled and pantile covered roof. It had a lucam in the east side of the roof, also covered with pantiles and at the southern end a brick built chimney stack. In the ridge of the roof, near the southern end, was a square-shaped louvred ventilator which was no doubt installed when the conversion to weaving took place.

Prior to conversion the mill had six pairs of stones, two wheels and a six foot fall.[4] Several looms were installed in the building and at least four pairs of stones retained (sic)[5] which indicated it was a combined corn and weaving mill. Indeed the mill is designated a "Drabbet Manufactury & Corn Mill" on the 1904 edition of the 25 inch Ordnance Survey Map.

Drabbet or Drabbett was a coarse cloth with linen warp and cotten weft. It was used in the making of smocks.[6] Given this use it is not surprising to find that the building also contained a Dye House. The Drabbet factory was established on the site in 1842 utilising the water power from the Waveney to operate the looms and other machinery through lay-shafting and pulleys.[7]

The waterwheel was cast iron with metal buckets and phosphor bronze bearings.[8] It appears it was a low-breast or Poncelet Wheel. Parts of the iron buckets can be seen supporting a bank on the opposite side of the road from the mill site. The pitwheel and other gear wheels were also of cast iron.

A description of the mill in the third decade of the 19th century is found in an advertisement which appeared in September 1826, following an earlier auction sale of a stock of wheat, flour, etc., by order of the Assignees under Harvey & Hills Bankruptcy.[9]

Syleham Water Corn Mill was advertised in September 1826 "To be sold or let for a term of years." The property was described as "All those Water Corn Mills, mansion residence, stable etc., and the Tolls arising from a Gate near the Mill, situated at Syleham, in the County of Suffolk. The mill, which has 6 feet fall of water, has two Water Wheels, two pit wheels, 6 pairs of stones, and all gears, capable of manufacturing 20 lasts of wheat per week (i.e. about 41 $\frac{1}{2}$ tons).* Possession at Michaelmas next."[10]

A further bankruptcy was reported in 1836 when a fiat in bankruptcy was made against "John Roper the elder late of Hoxne and Syleham in the County of Suffolk, miller and flour merchant." He had to surrender at The King's Head Inn, Beccles.[11] It is possible however that the mill referred to in this bankruptcy notice was the windmill and not the water mill.

An advertisement in the Suffolk Chronicle of the 8th August 1838, announced the mill was to be let. It described it as having 6 feet fall of water, 2 water wheels, 2 pit wheels, 6 pairs of stones and capable of manufacturing 20 lasts of wheat per week with the yearly average amounting to 14 lasts per week.

Drabbet manufacture was brought to Syleham by Henry Warne. In 1838

* See footnote on page 20.

Syleham Watermill, c. 1900.

Syleham Watermill. Photograph from the Cleer Alger Collection.
Courtesy of Suffolk Records Office.

Henry Warne had a factory in Mere Street, Diss where he employed 40 men, 20 boys and 3 women making drabbetts, huckabacks (a coarse variety of linen for towels, etc.) sheeting and shirting. Some of the men worked in their own homes and were paid up to 16s. per week for as many as 16 hours a day although the average wage was around 12s. per week. Around 1840 Henry Warne closed his factory at Diss and moved to Hoxne Mill.[12]

The Corn Mill at Hoxne was in the possession of one Thomas Coleby in 1844 and it would appear that Henry Warne was in partnership with him. However Warne later moved downstream to Syleham Mill where his business was described as "Henry Warne & Sons, Cotton & Linen Manufacturers, Syleham Mills".[13] It seems that in 1849 all the corn milling machinery and equipment was removed from the mill because an advertisement appeared in the Suffolk Chronicle on the 20th October of that year announcing an auction sale to take place on the 25th October. It stated, "The entire FITTINGS of the MILL, which is converted into a factory; including 11 French burr 4–feet Millstones, in excellent preservation and of good quality; flour mill, jumper, vats, with hoppers &c; face and spur wheels, hoop iron, oak shafts and an assortment of cast-iron and wood wheels; stone-nuts, with wrought-iron spindles, and other effects, the property of Mr. HENRY WARNE." By the 1851 census Warne is described as a drabbet manufacturer employing 96 persons[14] and by 1855 sheeting and shirting manufacture had been added to his trading activities.[15]

Henry Warne died on the 8th November 1852 and by his Will dated the 3rd July 1851, he appointed his wife Sarah and his son Charles his Executrix and Executor respectively. His Will recited, inter alia, "I give and bequeath unto my said wife and my son Charles — my Executrix and Executor ALL the Machinery in the Mill of every description also everything belonging to the Dying House Bleaching House Drying House and Calender together with all carts waggons gigs horses and harness to enable them to carry on the business now conducted by me at Syleham Mill under the firm of Sarah Warne and Son . . ." His Will also recited "I further direct that in case my said wife should cease to remain my widow by marrying again or by death all her interest in the business shall cease and the Machinery in the mill with everything belonging to the Dying House Drying House Bleaching House and Calender together with the carts waggons gigs horses and harness and the entire business shall belong to my son Charles for his own absolute use and benefit and disposal."
16

It would therefore seem likely that the business at Syleham Mill was continued for a time by Mrs. Sarah Warne and her son Charles. Later it appears Charles Warne entered into partnership with Frederick Payne. This would have been prior to 1862. However, an official notice was published stating that the "Partnership between Charles Warne and Frederick Payne, as manufacturers of Drabbetts and other fabrics, at Syleham Mill, Co. of Suffolk, dissolved 15

July 1862. The business will be continued by the said Charles Warne alone."[17] In August 1862 another official notice appeared which announced that provisional protection was allowed to Charles Warne "of Syleham Mills, near Scole, Co. of Norfolk," for the invention of "improvements in the manufacture of linen drabbett".[18] No information has so far been discovered as to what the improvements were. In any event Charles Warne was also operating as a miller at the same time. In 1864 he is described as a linen manufacturer and corn miller.[19]

However, in 1865 and also in 1868 and 1869, Charles Warne was still conducting the business himself and was described as a "drabbett, linen and smock manufacturer by water and steam power."[20]

Charles Warne became insolvent in 1872 and Messrs. George Chase*, Edwards and Adolphus Holmes assumed control of the business and continued making drabbett, shirting, sheeting and huckaback.[21] They are listed in Trade Directories of 1873, 1874 and 1885 as drabbett manufacturers using both steam and water power.[22] Later and by 1888 and through to 1892, the Syleham Drabbett Co., "linen and smock manufacturers," owned the mill when Edward A. Holmes, was the manager.[23]

The mill was offered for sale by public auction in 1872 but failed to attract a purchaser. The Auction Sale Particulars state that the mill was a "substantial structure with spacious floors, the greater part being occupied by Weaving looms." The Particulars also describe the premises as including an engine and boiler house, a 16ft diameter wheel, counting house, warehouse, three pairs of stones for grinding corn and accommodation for dyeing and drying. A building across the road from the mill was used for drying, the floors being slatted and it had tenters on which dyed cloth was stretched to dry. In the mill building the looms were on the ground floor and spinning machines on the first floor. The second floor was used for preparation purposes and the corn mill area was at the western end of the premises. Both water and steam power was used to drive the machinery but steam power was used only when the water level was too low to operate the wheel.[24] The mill was then leased by the Executors of the late Henry Warne, the lease expiring on the 11th October 1899, to Messrs. E.A. Holmes & Co. At some time during the term of this lease, the property was offered for sale again, the particulars stating "For upwards of 60 years successfully carried on by the Proprietors the late Messrs. H. & C. Warne, and at present in the occupation of Messrs. E.A. Holmes & Co., whose lease expires on October 11th 1899 when possession will be given." Apart from the details of the premises and other parts of the estate (See Appendix B) the particulars also state, "N.B. — The mill and Factory are now in full work and

*George Chase who was a farmer, landowner, merchant, and miller at Mendham Watermill where he was in partnership with John Munnings.

Syleham Watermill. After the disastrous fire of 24th May, 1928.
Courtesy of Mrs Martin.

Needham Watermill, c. 1900. Courtesy of Mrs Morton Denny.

employ from 80 to 100 hands, and the present tenants are willing to treat with intending hirers or purchasers for the taking over of the business as a going concern, also for the goodwill, Book Debts, Stock-in-Trade, Machinery, &c., &c. The returns based on an average of the past 3 years are about £9000 per annum."[25]

Mr. E.A. Holmes obviously retired from business when his lease expired in 1899. It would seem he must have resided at Southwold on the Suffolk coast, maybe after retiring, because in 1909 he was Mayor of the then Borough of Southwold and he consented to serve in that civic office for a second term.[26]

In 1899 William Emms bought the mill[27] and the firm was then known as William Emms & Sons. In 1900 and again in 1904 the firm was styled "SYLEHAM DRABBETT CO., Frederick George Emms, Manager, Linen & Ready Made Clothing Manufacturer, Syleham Mills."[28] Later Ernest Richard Emms took over; he was the son of William but he preferred to call the firm Richard Emms & Co. as opposed to Ernest Emms & Co.! Eventually his son, Ernest George Emms took over after working with his father.[29]

Sales of drabbett declined in the years before the First World War and the village's long association with the linen industry finally came to an end at the outbreak of war in 1914.[30]

Whilst Mr. E.R. Emms and his son, Mr. E.G. Emms were in Ipswich on the 24th May (Empire Day) 1928, a message was relayed to them requesting them to return to Syleham forthwith. The mill was on fire and subsequently destroyed together with part of the Drabbett Factory and the Toll Cottage. It was thought that the fire was started by an overheated bearing.[31] The Harleston Fire Brigade attended with Captain Robert Pipe in charge. He was injured when a brick wall collapsed on him and he was trapped in the debris suffering leg injuries. He was admitted to hospital but seven days afterwards he collapsed and died at the age of 57. On Monday 23rd November 1987 a citation and photograph of Captain Pipe was unveiled at Harleston Fire Station by the Norfolk Chief Fire Officer in the presence of two grand-daughters of Captain Pipe, Mr. Ernest George Emms and others — 60 years after the event! The hero of Syleham Mill fire had been forgotten over the years until the event was mentioned by the late Morton Denny of Harleston; after this, research was carried out by the Supervising Officer for Harleston, Mr. R. Crickmore.[32] The corn mill and Toll cottage were not rebuilt but the damaged part of the Drabbett Factory was reconstructed. After 1914 only ready-made men's garments were made and indeed still are at the time of writing (1989).

By at least 1959 the firm was known as Richard Emms Ltd. Clothing Manufacturers. In 1969 Mr. E.G. Emms sold the business to a Mr. Robert Hurst who was a member of the Carrington-Viyella Group. They occupied the premises and carried on the business for about two years and in 1971 they in turn sold to Messrs. F.W. Harmer & Co.[33] This latter firm was an old-established

Norwich concern going back nearly 165 years. It was one of the City's oldest
family firms which had other factories at Diss and Fakenham and a subsidiary
in Stradbroke apart from the Syleham premises. In February 1989 the firm's
future was in doubt and so restructuring of production was carried out to
increase profitability.[34] After a world-wide search for a buyer without success,
in the following December, Harmers announced they were axing nearly 470
jobs following massive losses — almost 300 at Norwich, about 70 at Fakenham
and 100 at Syleham, and therefore closing down the long-established and well-
known family firm, blaming cheap foreign imports and high interest rates for
this adverse and much regretted turn of events.[35] And so the long history of the
Syleham Mill site ended, unfortunately, on a very sad note.

SYLEHAM WATERMILL

1.   Augustine Page, "A Supplement to the Suffolk Traveller," 1844, p.421.
2.   John Munnings, "The Passing of the Country Miller and his Mill, Rivers
      Stour and Waveney," unpublished article, c.1970.
3.   Sun Fire Insurance Policy No. 415720. (Vol.275).
4.   Rex Wailes, "Suffolk Watermills," Excerpts Transactions of the
      Newcomen Society, 1964–1965, p.101.
5.   Mr. E.G. Emms of Pulham Market, information supplied 2.12.1987.
6.   Nesta Evans, "The East Anglian Linen Industry, Rural Industry and
      Local Economy 1500–1850" and Glossary.
      Chambers 20th Century Dictionary.
7.   Mr. E.G. Emms, Op. Cit..
8.   Ibid.
9.   Ipswich Journal, February 11th 1826.
10.   Ipswich Journal, September 2nd 1826.
11.   London Gazette, August 16th 1836.
12.   Nesta Evans, Op. Cit. pp. 154, 155.
13.   White's Directory, 1844.
14.   Nesta Evans, Op. Cit. p.156.
15.   White's Directory 1855.
16.   Norfolk Record Office, NCC Wills 1853 OW36.
17.   London Gazette, July 29th 1862.
18.   London Gazette, August 15th 1862.
19.   Harrod & Co.'s Directory 1864.
20.   Kelly's Directory 1865 & 1869; Morris' Directory 1868.
21.   Eric Pursehouse, "Waveney Studies," reprint 1983, p.186.
22.   Harrod's Directory 1873 and White's Directories 1874 and 1885.
23.   Kelly's Directories 1888 and 1892.
24.   Nesta Evans, Op.Cit., p.157.

Advertisement from the Harleston Almanac, 1914.

Weybread Watermill, c. 1900. Suffolk Photo Survey, courtesy Museum of East Anglian Life, Stowmarket.

25. George Durrant & Sons, Auctioneers & Estate Agents, Harleston, Norfolk, undated Sale particulars, but pre 1899.
26. The Miller, November 14th 1910.
27. Nesta Evans, Op. Cit., p. 158.
28. Kelly's Directories, 1900 and 1904.
29. Mr. E.G. Emms, Op. Cit.
30. Nesta Evans, Op. Cit., p. 158.
31. Mr. E.G. Emms, Op. Cit.
32. Harleston & Waveney Express, November 27th 1987 and Diss Mercury & Advertiser, November 27th 1987.
33. Mr. Hubert Bush of Needham, Norfolk, grandson of Mr. Arthur H. Bush, one time owner and occupier of Needham Watermill.
34. Eastern Daily Press, February 8th 1989.
35. Eastern Daily Press, December 9th 1989.

Luck's Watermill, Suffolk

NGR TM225805

This mill, which disappeared some considerable time ago, was situated about a mile south of the village of Needham and approached from the A143 road via a loke and over marshes. All that is now left are two brick arches and some other brickwork at ground level. The mill pond and leat are still there but somewhat overgrown and choked. The mill house and other outbuildings that once existed have also gone. It stood less than half a mile upstream from Needham Mill.

Remarkably little information concerning this mill is available, in fact after exhaustive enquiries and not a little research, no details have so far been discovered, except that it is said to have had two pairs of stones.[1] It must have been quite a small mill, probably the smallest on the Waveney.

The mill is shown on Kirby's map of Suffolk 1736, Bowen's map of Suffolk 1760, Faden's maps of Suffolk 1783 and Norfolk 1797 but on A. Bryant's map of 1824/25 it is shown as "LOWER MILL," whereas on Bryant's map of 1826 it is named "WEYBREAD MILL" notwithstanding further downstream another mill is also shown as "WEYBREAD MILL". The latter was always known as such. On the first edition of the Ordnance Survey 1 inch map 1837/38 it is designated "LOW MILL". The designations of Lower Mill and Low Mill are somewhat contradictory since this mill is really the upper of the two Weybread mills.

In 1855 one John Pollard is listed as a corn miller at Weybread in a Trade Directory and he could have operated Luck's Mill. The only reason given for this supposition is that he is not mentioned in connection with either Needham Mill or Weybread Mill a mile or so north of Weybread Church.[2]

The mill is also shown on the Ordnance Survey 6 inch map 1885 Norfolk Sheet CXI NW Suffolk Sheet XXVI NW, as "Luck's Mill (Corn)." However, on the Ordnance Survey 25 inch sheet 1904, Norfolk CXI, 2, Suffolk XXVI, 2, buildings are shown and designated "Luck's Mill Farm" and the bridge over the River Waveney at this point is named "Lucksmill Bridge". The mill was very

Weybread Watermill, c. 1895. Courtesy of Mr K Palmer.

Mendham Watermill, c. 1912. Courtesy Mr Fred Hadingham.

much on the Suffolk side of the river.

The late Mr. Albert Sidney Bush of Needham (who died on 13th November 1988, aged 91), son of the late Mr. Arthur H. Bush (the latter owned Needham Mill), said he was told Luck's Mill was originally a Flax Mill and was never a corn or grist mill. Furthermore it was a small mill and had disappeared before his father arrived in the village in 1897. It would therefore be reasonable to assume that Luck's Mill was demolished somewhere between 1885 and 1897. Perhaps this mill started life as a Flax Mill and was later converted to a Corn mill. However there does seem to be sufficient evidence for concluding that the mill was a corn mill, certainly it was so at the end of its days.

In a book entitled "Diss The Pictorial Past 1860–1908" by Cyril Piper, photograph No. 65 is of Bandmaster Luck of The Diss Rifle Volunteers who lead the band for many years. Could he have been a relation or descendant of the owner/occupier of this mill?

LUCK'S WATERMILL

1. "Mills Past and Present on the River Waveney" (author unknown) copy supplied by Rank Hovis Ltd.
2. White's History & Gazetteer & Directory of Suffolk, 1855.

Needham Watermill, Suffolk

NGR TM229811

There is little doubt that the forerunner of the present mill was timber-framed and weatherboarded and dated back to at least 1611 when it was called Fryer's mill and at that time belonged to George Hering of Norwich.

A mill must have existed in Needham well before 1611 because "the abbot and convent of Sibton in Suffolk had a fishery and a watermill called Fryer's Mill, in this place (Needham) which was let with their grange and manor of Weybrede in Suffolk."[1] Sibton Abbey was founded in 1150 by William FitzRobert for monks of the Cistercian Order. Prior to the Dissolution the Abbey was offered to Thomas, Duke of Northumberland. It was held by his family until 1611 when it was purchased by John Scrivener.[2]

A century and a quarter elapses before we come to the next authentic date, that of 1736, when the mill appears on Kirby's map of Suffolk. It also is shown on Bowen's map of Suffolk of 1760, Faden's map of Suffolk of 1783 and on Faden's map of 1797 of Norfolk as "Sparrow's Mill", presumably the name of the then owner and/or occupier. The position of this mill is shown on Bryant's map of 1826 although unnamed. The mill is again clearly shown on the first edition of the Ordnance Survey 1 inch map of 1837/38.

The Mill, outbuildings and mill cottage are situated about a half mile south-east of the centre of the village and abuts the somewhat narrow road leading to Instead Manor House. It is in fact situated in the Parish of Weybread. (The village of Needham is in Norfolk whereas its watermill stands on the south side of the river and just in Suffolk).

Sometime prior to 1835 John Neale appears to have been the miller here and he also ran the nearby Post Windmill (situated about a quarter of a mile south of the watermill). An auction sale of the mill and windmill was arranged to take place on the 12th August 1835, on behalf of the executors of the late John Neale and was advertised in the Suffolk Chronicle. It is quite clear a sale was not effected. After the mills were advertised to be let in the same newspaper in May of the following year, John Neale's executors again offered the mills for sale. This was in May of 1837 when the mill and windmill were advertised "To be sold by Private Contract". Both mills were described as "fitted up and in good condition, lying in Weybread, Suffolk and Needham, Norfolk."[3] It is uncertain as to whether the mill was actually sold when offered in 1837 but in Trade Directories of 1858 and 1863 George Chase is cited as "Butcher, miller and farmer" in Needham.[4]

Mr. G.H. Prentice was the farmer and miller at this mill in 1868.[5] Two years later in 1870 or perhaps a little earlier, the mill was rebuilt in brick after a fire.[6] Then in 1888 Thomas William Coleby was the miller,[7] followed by the brothers John and William Button by 1892 [8] who were also millers at Weybread Watermill and at Diss. The tower windmill at Victoria Road, Diss was bought in July 1880 by John Button and he also worked postmills nearby.[9] It seems that Robert James Kemp was the next miller at Needham[10] although from records it appears he was there for a very short time.

Two years later in 1898 Arthur Henry Bush rented the mill from January of that year.[11]

Mr. A.H. Bush was a millwright by trade and worked in the foundry of E.J. Knights of Harleston,[12] the firm who supplied waterwheels and machinery to several of the Waveney Mills. He continued as tenant, presumably on a yearly basis, until he took an eight year lease from the 11th October 1914, at a "yearly rent of Forty Five Pounds". By the Indenture dated 20th February 1915, his landlords are stated to be John Anthony Everson of Harleston, Merchant, and John Farrow Betts of Norwich, Gentleman, (executors of Henry Drane, deceased), and they agreed "to demise and let to the Tenant All that the messuage or dwellinghouse with the water corn mill adjoining commonly called Needham Mill and the yards gardens stables sheds and other buildings to the said messuage and mill respectively belonging AND also the whole of the machinery tackle fixtures and apparatus in and about the said mill and dwellinghouse . . . AND also the several enclosures of arable and pasture land near or adjoining the said mill as all the said premises situate together partly at Weybread in Suffolk and partly at Needham in Norfolk are now in the occupation of the tenant and contain together fourteen acres or thereabouts . . ." Part of the property was copyhold tenure and as such was held from year to year on licence from the Lords of the Manors for a term of seven years.

As tenant, Mr. Bush, covenanted "to keep the inside of the said dwellinghouse mill and buildings and the glass in and about the said mill (and the articles specified in the Schedule Hereto) and all the gates rails and fences and ditches belonging to the premises in good and tenantable repair and condition and so to leave the same at the expiration of the tenancy (damage by fire excepted) being allowed the Landlord's rough materials for the purpose Provided that should it be absolutely necessary during the Tenancy to provide a new waterwheel* or shaft or main driving wheels or stones the same shall be done

* The Wheel was internal.

at the Landlord's expense the tenant paying one third of the cost of labour". He further covenanted "to use and work the Mill as a Cornmill continuously during the Tenancy for grinding wheat barley and such like grains and so as to retain and extend trade carried on thereat and not for any other purpose except occasionally grinding of small seeds and not to use the said Mill as a shelling mill and for any purposes which would render the same hazardous as a Water Corn mill or deteriorate as such the value thereof or prejudice or affect the assurance thereof against fire". The Landlords were responsible for the upkeep of the main structure of the Mill and dwellinghouse.

The Schedule to the Indenture is very informative and makes most interesting reading, there being considerable detail of the mill's contents and machinery. That part of the Schedule relating to the actual mill is given in full at Appendix C.

In 1918 Mr. Bush's Landlords decided to dispose of the mill, mill cottage, outbuildings and land and so, on the 5th June 1918, the whole of the property was offered for sale by public auction in one lot by Messrs. George Durrant & Sons at The Magpie Hotel, Harleston "at 4 O'clock precisely in the Afternoon". At the same time other property was offered, including Weybread Mill.

The Mill is described in the Auctioneers' sale particulars as a "Brick and Tile Four Storey Water-power Corn Mill fitted with 4 pairs French Burr Stones, One pair 4ft. 4ins. and three pairs 4ft., Waterwheel and Driving Gear, all of which will be included in the Sale". The present mill building is actually built with red brick laid Flemish Bond and the tiles are blue pantiles. Windows have segmental brick arches to the ground and first floor. The lucam which was at the south gable end has been removed. There was "A Capital Set of Brick and Tile Outbuildings, including stabling for 4 Horses, Cart Lodge, 2 Gig Houses, Cow House with Granary over, and Cattle Shed and Yard". The "Comfortable Dwelling House" had three bedrooms and the property extended to 14 acres 3 roods 8 perches, the majority being freehold tenure except 4 acres and 2 roods which was copyhold tenure.

Bidding in the Sale Room started at £300 and progressed to £350, £375, £400, £425, £430, £435, £440 and finally £450; the property being bought by the tenant, Mr. A.H. Bush. Mrs. Arthur Bush had recently been left some money by a relative and this enabled her husband to bid for and purchase the Mill. He then continued in business as a "Miller and Merchant" until 1934 and, according to an advertisement in the Harleston Almanac of 1914 he supplied "Best Quality at Lowest Prices in Roller and Stone Flour, Corn, Meals, Offals, Malt, Hops, Etc. Grists Ground & Oats crushed. Orders personally supervised and Promptly Executed. Boats to Let. Mineral Water & Light Refreshments". He was obviously an enterprising man and it appears he conducted "a very thriving business, working day and night". He used to employ four men, two of them fetching corn from the farms and returning the same when ground.

They used to cover an area (sic) (radius?) of eight miles . . . [13] Mr. Albert Sidney Bush (a son of the miller) said that three of the four sets of stones were used for grinding corn and "a special set for grinding wheat for flour".[14] There are still two French Burr Stones each with its iron band in the path of the Mill Cottage, obviously those from the mill. Mr. Bush took 3lbs. grist for every coomb ground as his toll. As a boy Mr. Albert Bush helped his father in the mill, "You had to in those days". After serving in the Royal Norfolk Regiment from 1915 until the end of the Great War, he worked with his father in the mill for a while as he was unable to find employment.

The river was very low at times during summer months with insufficient fall to work the waterwheel. In order to keep going during such periods, a portable engine was used which was bought by Mr. A.H. Bush who also installed a hammer mill "which never ground corn as fine as the stones".[15]

During Mr. Bush's tenancy he experienced one of the worst floods that occurred in the Waveney Valley. This was in the summer of 1912 when the water rose to the height of the fifth stair in the house and a similar height in the mill. The water was so high that the Bush family were confined to the first floor of the mill cottage and of course the mill could not be worked. Eventually it was decided to vacate the cottage. Mr. Albert Bush relates: "The boat we had was lodged against a wooden bridge 200 yards from the mill, so as father and I were the only ones able to swim, we managed to get into the mill. From the first floor we opened the door where the carts used to be loaded up, and we slid into the water, swam to the boat which was half submerged, got it floating and took it round to the house, loaded my mother, sister Rose and brother Fred into it and rowed them across to my Uncle Fred's at Instead Hall Farm. We had to stay three weeks as the house was in such a filthy state."[16] Mr. Arthur Bush continued at the mill until around 1934,[17] when he sold it to Sqd. Ldr. Brown from Pulham. He in turn sold the property to Mr. Braybrook in 1961 but before disposing of the property, Sqd. Ldr. Brown sold all the iron machinery including the waterwheel, in 1940 for scrap — towards the war effort. The next owners of the mill in 1971 were Mr. and Mrs. Morriati who converted the mill into a residence and they sold it to Mrs. Jennie Collyer from London. The only section of machinery in situ is part of the sack hoist gear. "In 1963 the mill was converted to a gauging station. The old mill wheel flume was made into a 10 foot wide flow measurement weir. At the same time a new structure was built on the bypass channel upstream of the mill containing a 3 foot-wide weir for low flow measurement, and a 25 foot weir for high flows. This replaced the derelict weir and flood sluice. The scheme was also designed to produce land drainage benefits and to reduce flooding by increasing the flood discharge capacity from 450 to 750 cubic feet per second. The total cost was £12,714.00."[18]

The Mill Cottage was offered for sale at a "price guide of £175,000" and sold in 1988.

The Mill Cottage stands close to the mill and at its south-east end. The northern half of the cottage, which is timber framed, is of considerable age being contemporary with the original mill, i.e., that which was destroyed by fire. When being shown round the Mill Cottage, certain charred timbers were pointed out. These were in the north-west wall and so were very close to the mill itself. This being so, it must have been 'touch and go' as to whether the cottage would suffer the same fate as the mill. Some time ago the cottage was extended at the rear, in fact it was more or less doubled in size. This addition was probably made when the mill was rebuilt.

In June 1990, the mill was advertised for sale by private treaty by Messrs. Strutt & Parker of Norwich at an asking price in the region of £245,000. Unsold at this price, it was offered by Partridge and Lucas of Eye, Suffolk, in October 1990 at £215,000.

NEEDHAM WATERMILL

1.   Blomefield's "History of Norfolk", 1806, Vol. V, p.374.
2.   William A. Dutt, "Suffolk", 1933, p.276.
3.   Ipswich Journal, 11th May 1837.
4.   Post Office Directory 1858 and Harrod's Directory 1863.
5.   J.G. Harrod & Co.'s Directory.
6.   Rex Wailes, "Suffolk Watermills", Excerpts Transactions of the Newcomen Society 1964–1965, p.111.
7.   The Rev. C. Mather, "Some Notes on Needham", 1974, p.26.
8.   Kelly's Directory.
9.   Harry Apling, "Norfolk Windmills", Vol. I, 1984, p.92.
10. The Rev. C. Mather, Op.Cit.
11. Albert S. Bush, "Needham Notes or The Memoirs of a Miller's Son", 1988, p.1.
12. Ibid. p.1.
13. Ibid. p.1.
14. Ibid. p.1.
15. Ibid. p.1.
16. Ibid. p.2.
17. The Rev. C. Mather, Op.Cit, p.10.
18. Ibid.

Weybread Watermill Suffolk

NGR TM241819

The earliest reference to a watermill at Weybread is in Domesday Survey — "WEIBRADA And 1 Mill". Although Prof. H.C. Darby in "The Domesday Geography of Eastern England", 3rd Edition 1971 page 190 states:-
"5 mills 1 settlement. The group of 5 mills was at Weybread; the Domesday Book records only 4 mills and three-quarters of another (329b), but there was a quarter of a mill at the adjoining village of Instead (447) and this may be the missing fraction." So there was more than one mill at Weybread but this surely refers to the Parish of Weybread in which Instead would also lie and the mill in this latter village is probably that at Needham. Another could well have been the site of Luck's Mill which also lies in the same parish.

In 1703 the Weybread Hall Manor and Estate was purchased by Jennings Booty, a yeoman, and the Instead Manor by William Cook, the owner of the Water Mill. This could well be the Weybread Mill.[1]

Weybread Mill is shown on Kirby's map of 1736, Bowen's map of 1760, Faden's map of 1783, Faden's map of 1797 (as Waybred Mill), Bryant's maps of 1824–26 and the first edition of the Ordnance Survey 1 inch map 1837/8 (as Water Mill).

William Mann of Syleham, Suffolk, miller, corn merchant and farrier, who ran Syleham watermill, also ran Weybread watermill and on 30th June 1779 he insured his "Water Corn Mill and going gears therein timber and tiled £400. Utensils and stock £300."[2] By 1785 Jacob Stanton was the miller at this mill and he was also a baker. On the 7th May of that year he insured "his dwelling-house and baking office adjoining situate at Harleston in the Co. of Norfolk in his own tenure, brick stud and tiled £200".[3] Unfortunatley, within the next ten years Jacob Stanton was to suffer a financial calamity.

On the 21st April 1794, Jacob Stanton had to surrender at the Three Tuns Inn, Bungay, as a consequence of a "Commission of Bankrupt" awarded against him.[4] Then on the 19th June of the same year his creditors met the Assignees of his estate at the Three Tuns Inn, Bungay.[5]

Two months later an official announcement appeared as follows:-

"To be sold by auction by order of the Assignees of Jacob Stanton, a Bankrupt, at the Swan Inn in Harleston, in the Co. of Norfolk, on 27th August 1794.

Lot 1.   A capital Freehold Water Corn Mill, called Weybread Two Mills, situated in Weybread, in the county of Suffolk, late in the Use of the said Jacob Stanton, with two Water Wheels, Five Pair of Stones, Two Flour Mills, and cylinder therein, and capacious Corn Chambers capable of containing 50 to 60 Lasts of Corn, and every conveniency for carrying on an Extensive trade. Also a new-invented Engine for cutting Straw and Hay, worked by the Water Wheel, by which a great Quantity may be cut in a short Time. Also a good Dwelling House near the Mills, Workshop, handsome Gardens, Stable and about three Acres of rich Meadow Land lying contiguous thereto. The above Premises are in good Repair.

Lot 2.   A Post Wind-Mill, near the above Mill, situate upon Shotford Heath, late in the Use of the said Jacob Stanton, with one pair of French stones. Mr. Gillingwater, Harleston, will show the above premises.

Lot 3.   A Post Wind-Mill, with two pair of stones, situate at Pulham St. Mary the Virgin, in the county of Norfolk late in the Use of the said Jacob Stanton, and the Piece of enclosed land whereon the Mill is erected. Possession of all the premises may be had immediately."[6]

It is interesting that in the auction particulars of sale this mill it is called Weybread Two Mills, presumably because of the two waterwheels.

It appears sales were effected because an announcement was published in December 1794, as follows:-

"Commission of Bankrupt Jacob Stanton, of Weybread, Co. of Suffolk, Miller. Dividend 19 January next at the Three Tuns Inn, Bungay.[7] The Certificate to be granted on or before 20 January next."[8]

The final chapter in the Jacob Stanton bankruptcy saga was the announcement in 1796 to the effect that a Final Dividend was to be paid on the 24th May at the Three Tuns Inn, Bungay.[9]

Jacob Stanton's bankruptcy was in all probability brought about by the economic situation prevailing at that time. Most of the country was adversely affected by the financial instability and both the scarcity and high price of food in 1795 and 1796. The harvests of 1795 were deficient as they were in other countries but supplies which might have come from abroad and given a measure of relief were not available. In any event our relations at the time with Holland and France precluded any supplies from these two countries being imported.

It would be fair to presume that being bankrupt Jacob Santon's career as a wind and water miller was at an end. However, on the 25th May 1799 an announcement appeared in the Bury & Norwich Post to the effect that Weybread Mill was to be offered for sale by auction on the 6th June. It was described as having two water wheels, five pairs of stones, one machine and two flour mills. Interested parties were requested to enquire of Mr. Jacob Stanton, on the premises. Perhaps he somehow continued at the mill for at least another five years after the "Commission of Bankrupt" was awarded.

In the Ipswich Journal of September 28th 1816 was an advertisement — "Wanted at Weybread Mill by Mr. John Cook, two men, one as a flour dresser, and the other to dress stones." Almost five years later a similar advertisement appeared in the same newspaper dated 16th June 1821 — "Wanted, a miller and stone dresser at John Cook's, Weybread." Which Mill John Cook occupied is not known for certain. It could well have been either Luck's Mill, Needham Watermill, Weybread Watermill or the Post Windmill at Weybread. However, the following advertisement appeared on April the 21st 1821 — "To be sold by auction some time this month. A dwelling house, Water Corn Mill, situate in Weybread, Suffolk, now in the occupation of the Executors of William Mann, deceased, under a lease which will expire the 10th October, 1827."[10] It would therefore be feasible for John Cook to have occupied Weybread Watermill as a sub-tenant of the Executors of William Mann.

Weybread Mill was again offered for sale by auction at the Mart, London, on the 19th May 1828 "by order of the Proprietor". It was described — "The Weybread Corn Mill on the River Waveney. The mill is partly brick, and the remainder timber built, and contains five floors, 7 pairs of stones, flour mill etc., situated at Weybread, Suffolk."[11]

Then on the 23rd August 1828, the mill was advertised in the Suffolk Chronicle to be let.

At sometime during the first half of the 19th century the mill was occupied by Messrs. Cocks and Sims. They were mentioned as being millers at Weybread in 1838.[12] On the 16th January 1841, the mill was offered for sale by auction at the Royal Hotel, Market Place, Norwich. On that occasion the advertisement stated — "All that superior Board and Tile Water Corn Mill at Weybread, in Suffolk, capable of manufacturing 25 lasts of corn per week (i.e. about 52 tons)* containing five floors, two Water Wheels, one of which is 20 feet in diameter, and 10 feet wide, with a fall of 6 feet, driving six pairs of French stones, Smith's Patent Flour and other machines. The mill is now in full trade, in the occupation of Messrs. Cocks and Sims whose tenancy expires at Lady Day next, when possession will be given. Apply to Mr. John Sims on the premises."[13]

In 1842,[14] 1844,[15] 1855[16] and 1858[17] Henry Drane is listed as a miller at Weybread in various trade directories and it therefore seems that he pur-

* See footnote on page 20.

chased the Weybread watermill in January 1841 and took possession on Lady Day (25th March) on the expiration of Messrs. Cocks and Sims' tenancy.

An advertisement in the Suffolk Chronicle of the 27th July 1857, stated the mill was to be sold by auction on the 5th August 1857, by the executors of the late Mr. Wm. Cook, Gentleman, and that it had "been for many years in the hands of the present respectable tenant, Mr. Robert Bacon, whose term expires at Michaelmas, 1858". It is not known if the mill was sold by auction but Robert Bacon obviously continued to occupy the mill after Michaelmas 1858 because he was still the tenant when the mill was advertised on the 4th June 1859, in the Suffolk Chronicle as to be let. At that time it was capable of manufacturing 250 quarters of corn per week.

By 1865 Octavious Henry Prentice had taken over this mill and he certainly continued through to 1869.[18] However it is interesting to note that Robert John Neeve is also mentioned as being a miller at Weybread at the same time, i.e. 1865,[18] also in 1868,[19] 1869,[18] 1873[20] and 1874.[21] Quite which mill he operated is difficult to say since both Luck's Mill and Needham Mill were situated in the Civil Parish of Weybread and have at times been loosely termed Weybread mills. In addition there were, of course, windmills close by. However, in 1873[20] Robert John Neeve is listed under Weybread as "miller, water mills," but this does not tell the actual mill he occupied, but we can be certain he did not own or occupy as tenant the Weybread watermill but it is possible he might have been an employee at this mill, maybe as manager.

The commercial trade directories published between 1844 and 1920 cite various names as being the millers at Weybread but it is obvious some of them were windmillers.

However, "Chase & Munnings also had Weybread Mill;" they were certainly in occupation by 1879 when they were described as "millers and cattle condiment manufacturers."[22] They relinquished occupation after George Chase was killed in Harleston in 1887 after which John and William Button* rented the mill. The firm was known as J. & W.E. Button through to 1916.[23]

The death of Mr. William Edmund Chaplyn Button of Weybread Water Mills, who for some time past had been in failing health, took place in April 1893. He was the eldest son of Mr. John Button of Salisbury House, Diss.[24] Then in August 1902, Mr. John Button, William's brother who carried on at Weybread and Diss mills, died at the age of 72.[25]

In 1918 the mill was offered for sale by auction on behalf of the executors of Henry Drane, on the 5th June by George Durrant & Sons at the Magpie Hotel, Harleston, the mill was then under "Government Control" and in the occupation of Mr. John Benjamin Button at the apportioned yearly rental of £65 under a lease for 8 years from the 11th October 1914. The lease contained

---

* William Button also ran a Windmill at Weybread, (Kelly's Directory 1883).

covenants to the effect that the Lessee was to maintain "all the machinery and fixtures, Utensils, Tackle and Apparatus" specified in a Schedule "or which might thereafter be erected and put therein with the consent of the Lessors" in proper working condition and to leave it in such order and condition at the determination of the term. There was however a proviso which meant that the machinery, fixtures etc., had to be valued at the expiration of the term and if they amounted to less than £600 the Lessee had to pay as liquidated damages the amount that would make up that sum. On the other hand, if they were valued at more than £600 then the Lessors would pay the excess sum to the Lessee.

The property was stated to comprise the five-storey mill, "substantially built" of brick and timber, with a tile and slate roof and stated to be "in full trade" and capable of turning out 400 sacks per week, (i.e. about 50 tons of flour), with two water wheels: one wheel was 20 feet in diameter and said to be 12 feet wide, believed to be the largest on the River Waveney. It had just been "put in thorough repair". The second wheel was 16 feet in diameter. Both wheels were of cast iron construction with wooden floats and they were "included in the sale". In addition there was a "recently erected" brick and tile engine and boiler house with a 60ft. shaft; brick and tile stabling for six cart horses; three loose boxes; straw house; two riding horse stables; chaise house and a harness room with loft over. There was a Miller's Cottage (still standing) with sheds and gardens; a brick and slated family residence containing entrance hall, drawing room, dining room, breakfast room, office, kitchen, storeroom, pantry, landing, six bedrooms, cellar, scullery and coal house, flower and kitchen gardens; a pair of cottages with gardens in Wells Lane and at the time occupied by the horsemen; rich meadow land, the whole containing four acres or thereabouts. The sale particulars also state the fall of water "is upward of six feet and the power and capabilities of this Important Property are almost unequalled by any other of a similar description in the counties of Suffolk and Norfolk". It was a very large mill and obviously capable of considerable output.

The Schedule referred to in the Sale Particulars is as follows:-

1. Main Roller Shaft 44ft., Roller Shaft 15ft., 1 Barley Cylinder.
2. Two double sets Brake Rolls 24 x 9, two double sets Reduction Rolls 25 x 9, One double set Rolls 18 x 8, One No. 2 Victor Brush, One Oat Crusher (Turner's No. 17), Two pairs 4 foot Wheat Stones, One pair 4 foot Barley Stones, One Chaff Cutter (with necessary shafting).
3. Six Centrifugals, two sheets, Fan Exhaust, Eureka Wheat Cleaner with shaft and pulleys.
4. One Double Purifier, One inter Elevator Reel $2^1/_2$ sheets, One Single Purifier, One Flour Mixer, One Offal Mixer, One Vibrometer.
5. Inter Elevator Reel $3^1/_2$ sheets, Thirteen Sets Elevators and worm conveyors throughout the mill, One Horizontal 25 Horse-power Engine, One Cornish Boiler 30 Horse-power, Sack Hoist, Pulleys.

Bidding in the Sale Room started at £500 and progressed, in the main, by £25 bids, the whole property being bought by Mr. Button, the tenant, for £1250.

Before the roller plant ($4^1/_2$ sack) was fitted there were 10 pairs of stones which with a good head of water, could be driven by the two water wheels. The steam engine would then be left to drive the cleaning and dressing machinery.[26]

As the Auctioneers' Sale Particulars of 1918 correctly state this was a five-storey mill. It was in fact built of brick to first-floor level, timber framed with external white painted weather boarding from first-floor level to eaves level and up through the gable ends. The lucam was white weather boarded having curved brackets. The roofs were covered with pantiles. The windows had glazing bars and were side hung. There was a tall brick-built chimney stack to the engine house.

The red brick Georgian Mill House exists and is now a residential art centre and the miller's cottage still stands and is privately owned.

On Friday 6th February 1920, a disastrous fire occurred at the mill which resulted in its destruction including the machinery, plant and stocks of wheat and flour. The fire started shortly after 5.30 p.m. and by 6.00 p.m. the mill was well alight with flames reaching into the sky. Miss Mary Daniels of Weybread, who is 91 years of age, remembers the fire very well indeed. She could see the fire quite easily from a distance of $1^1/_2$ miles and walked to the mill with her brother. When she got there the front fell out and corn simply cascaded down onto the bridge and eventually spilled over into the river. Apparently the mill was full of both wheat and flour, the latter being stacked higher than usual because at the time sales were very slow. Later the wheat was dredged out of the river, kiln dried and sold at Harleston Sale Ground for chicken feed. Miss Daniels relates that her father bought 3 cwts of the corn and she thinks he paid 3s. 6d. ($17^1/_2$p) per bag.

There were of course no telephones in those days so Claude Aldridge who worked at the mill as a young man and was about 16 years old at the time, ran all the way to Harleston to call out the Fire Brigade. This was a horse-drawn engine and manually pumped. Unfortunately the Fire Brigade approached the mill via Wells Lane and therefore could not cross the river! They had to retrace their steps to some extent and cross the river by going over Shotford Bridge. By the time they arrived on the scene, they were met by a hopeless task and there was little they could do. Mr. Aldridge described the mill as being chock-a-block with flour with 300–400 10-stone bags of flour (18 to 25 tons) as the flour trade was bad at the time of the fire.

After reporting the fire, the Eastern Daily Press goes on to say "Mr. Button and his father and grandfather before him have carried on an extensive business at the mills for many years past, and when the property came into the market some two years ago Mr. Button became the purchaser. The loss, taking into account the valuable machinery, etc., and the heavy stocks of wheat and flour, must run into several thousand pounds".[27]

Prior to the fire, the mill used to grind poultry feed as well, very often running for 24 hours per day. The poultry feed was carted on to the marshes by the tumbril load to feed the numerous geese, etc.[28]

The mill was never rebuilt and all that remains as a reminder of this once powerful and well-known Waveney Mill, is the wheel race where the waters continue to run through and under the bridge as they did many years ago.

At the end of March 1989, The Mill House was offered for sale by private treaty by Savills of Norwich. It is described as a late 18th century 5-bedroomed house with the former coach house and adjacent outbuildings converted to artists' studios. It has gardens of about $^3/_4$ acre with river frontage and offers in the region of £325,000 were invited for the freehold.[29]

WEYBREAD WATERMILL

1. Augustine Page, "A Supplement to the Suffolk Traveller", 1844, p.p. 430.431.
2. Sun Fire Insurance Policy No. 415720 (Vol. 275).
3. Sun Fire Insurance Policy No. 504488 (Vol. 329).
4. London Gazette, April 5–8, 1794.
5. London Gazette, June 10–14, 1794.
6. London Gazette, August 9–12, 1794.
7. London Gazette, December 20–23, 1794.
8. London Gazette, December 27–30, 1794.
9. London Gazette, April 23–26, 1796.
10. Ipswich Journal, April 26, 1828.
12. Bury Post, September 10, 1838.
13. Norfolk Chronicle, January 2, 1841.
14. London Gazette, March 29, 1842, where he is mentioned as being a farmer, miller and brick maker and an assignee of a Redenhall Stone Mason.
15. White's Directory, 1844.
16. Ibid. 1855.
17. Post Office Directory, 1858.
18. Kelly's Directories, 1865, 1869.
19. Morris' Directory 1868.
20. Harrod & Co.'s Directory of Suffolk & Cambs., 1873.
21. White's Directory, 1874.
22. Kelly's Directory, 1879.
23. Ibid. 1916.
24. "The Miller", May 1 1893.
25. "The Miller", September 1 1902.

26. John Munnings, "The Passing of the Country Miller and his Mill, Rivers Stour and Waveney", unpublished Article, c. 1970.
27. Eastern Daily Press, 9 February 1920.
28. Mr. Ian A. Reeve of Dickleborough, Norfolk.
29. Eastern Daily Press, 24 and 31 March 1989.

Mendham Watermill, 1988. D F Pluck.

John Munnings, miller of Mendham Watermill and his four sons, left to right, William (farmer), Frederick (miller in succession to his father), Charles (emigrated to South Africa) and Alfred (the renowned artist).
Courtesy of Mr Fred Hadingham.

Mendham Watermill Suffolk

NGR TM271833

The Domesday Survey of 1086 gives "Menneham" "And 1 Mill." It is therefore quite possible that a mill existed hereabouts for over a thousand years.

Tithes of the mills of Mendham are mentioned in connection with the appropriation of the parish church of "Meaden-Ham" or "Myndham" to the Priory of the Holy Trinity at Ipswich in 1227.[1] In 1523 Robert Wythenham was the miller here.[2] He is included in a Return for Suffolk of those who paid the subsidy granted to Henry VIII in the fifteenth year of his reign.[3]

Robert Stanton was the miller at Mendham Mill in the early days of the eighteenth century. There was a Deed of Covenant to levy a fine by Edmund Eyre of Lammas, Norfolk, Gent., and others to Robert Stanton, miller, dated 26th March 1708 and it recites, inter alia, "All that Watermill situate being in Mendham aforesaid with the outhouses yards and Garden and Orchards and Lands and Meadows and pastures thereto belonging or reputed to be part now in the occupation of the said Robt. Stanton." The fine was also levied upon two messuages and lands in Wilby, Bedingfield, Redlingfield and Southolt.[4]

As would be expected the mill is shown on Kirby's map of 1736, Bowen's map of 1760, Hodskinson's Map of 1783 and Bryant's Map of 1824/5.

The present mill was built in 1807.[5] It was enlarged in 1871[6] at the NW end and at the same time it had a 25 h.p. beam engine installed by the makers Holmes & Sons of Norwich.[7] This engine, which provided auxilliary power to the water wheel, was of the old "Grasshopper" type but with compound cylinders and jet condensor. This engine gave exemplary service. The steam was generated in a Lancashire boiler, worked at 50lbs pressure, and was made by the Kirstall Forge Co., of Leeds; it too was installed in 1871.[8] The mill had only $3\frac{1}{2}$ feet fall of water and the internal low breast shot wheel of cast iron was 14 feet in diameter and 10 feet wide. It was made by Robert Knights of Harleston in 1861 and new gearing was also installed at this date.[9]

As far as can be ascertained the original 1807 mill comprised the gabled section containing the lucam.[10] It was then extended by the NW section which had ten windows and two doors in the front facade. The mill is of timber framed construction on a brick base and four storeys high. The exterior is clad with weather boarding under a glazed black pantile covered roof. Originally there were loading doors at first-floor level in both the original section and the extension, with entrance doors at ground-floor level in both. The windows in the front elevation were centre-pivoted; at the rear there were side-hung and centre-pivoted windows. The mill house of brick and tile construction with rendered elevations, immediately adjoins the mill on its SE end. There was a weathervane above the lucam with a fish and the four cardinal points and this still exists.

An official announcement appeared in September 1807 relating to the then miller at Mendham Watermill, one Stephen Spratt, concerning his bankruptcy. He had "to surrender on the 19th October at the House of George Cann, called the Cardinal's Hat, situate in Redenhall with Harleston, Norfolk".[11] Subsequently an auction sale of the mill was arranged to take place on the 13th January 1808. The advertisement described the property as "A commodious Water Mill with two pair of French stones, flour mill and gears. Also a valuable Bunching Mill,* worked by an extra Water Wheel, together with dwellinghouse, outbuildings, etc., situate in Mendham, Suffolk, late in the occupation of Mr. Stephen Spratt."[12] An announcement concerning the Commission of Bankrupt dated 22 September 1807, against Stephen Spratt, "late of Mendham, Co. of Suffolk, Miller," stated that the first and final dividend would be available on the 7th April 1809 at the Cardinal's Hat in Redenhall with Harleston, Norfolk.[13]

A most interesting advertisement appeared in September 1813 which clearly indicates that Mendham Watermill had at some time previously been converted from a corn mill to a textile mill, though it had a comparatively short life as the latter type of mill. This revealing advertisement reads as follows:—

"To be sold by auction at the White Swan Inn, St. Peter of Mancroft, Norwich on 25 September (1813)

Lot 1   A capital Watermill at Mendham, in the county of Suffolk, now employed in the Spinning of Worsted Yarn, with the gears and machinery therein, containing 874 Spindles, with preparing, roving, and other necessary apparatus used in the spinning of yarn. Also a dwellinghouse

---

* A mill in which the final beating of hemp is carried out prior to the process of heckling, i.e., the separating of the fibres which is the equivalent of combing wool. Bunching was done by hand originally but latterly carried out in mills using horse or water power. These mills were equipped with 'stampers' similar to those used in making paper.

Jimmy Souter, engine driver at Mendham Watermill for over 50 years.
Courtesy of Mr Fred Hadingham.

adjoining the mill, now in the occupation of Mr. James Sabberton, the proprietor, who will give possession at Michaelmas next.

The present water wheel, which is 14 feet by 8 feet, has been erected within the last three years upon new foundations, and drives through all floods. By the side of the wheel is a water lane, with a stream of sufficient power to work another wheel." [14]

The mill and house were not sold at auction because James Sabberton was still occupying the premises in December 1813. Indeed another auction sale was arranged to take place at The Tuns Inn, Bungay, on the 9th December 1813. It seems that the spinning of yarn was not considered to be an attractive commercial proposition as the advertisement announcing this latter auction sale stated that, "The premises are well adapted for corn or paper mills." It also announced that apart from the "very desirable Watermill" there was "a new built dwellinghouse in the occupation of Mr. James Sabberton and Samuel Tindall". Interested parties had to apply to Mr. James Sabberton on the premises. [15]

Whether or not the mill and house actually sold at auction is not known but clearly a sale was effected at some stage because in 1817 the property was in the ownership of Mr. John Norman. [16]

Incidentally, an announcement was made in January 1814 to the effect that the partnership between John Sabberton, James Sabberton and W. W. Parkinson, under the firm of John and James Sabberton & Company, Worsted Yarn Spinners, at Mendham Mills, in Mendham Suffolk and in the City of Norwich, was dissolved by mutual consent on the 21st December 1813. [17] After the dissolution of the partnership the mill obviously reverted to a corn mill, probably in 1814.

In 1830 Christopher Betts Johnson was mentioned as being the miller at Mendham Watermill. [18] He was born in 1783 and he and his wife Elizabeth had at least five sons and four daughters. He died on the 29th July 1839 aged 56 years. His wife died on the 5th January 1854 aged 70 years. Both were interred in the cemetery surrounding the United Reformed Chapel at Wortwell together with certain of their sons and daughters none of whom appear to have lived for more than 28 years, the eldest son William in fact died at the very early age of eleven years.

Another Christopher Betts Johnson is cited as the miller at Mendham in 1844, when he is also described as a farmer. [19] This is obviously a son of the previous miller by the same name and he (the son) continued at Mendham Mill until January 1853 by which time he appears to be in financial straits. An official announcement appeared on the 25th January 1853 describing Christopher Betts Johnson as of Wortwell, County of Norfolk and Mendham County of Suffolk, Miller, merchant and farmer and stated that by a deed dated 18th January 1853 he assigned all his estate for the benefit of creditors. [20]

However, Trade Directories of 1854, 1855 and 1858 mention him as the miller at Limbourne Mill, Wortwell. This Christopher Betts Johnson married Ellen Anne Barham and she died in 1852 aged 30 years. They had a son, Christopher Barham Johnson, who died in infancy in 1849. Ellen Anne Johnson also lies in the Wortwell cemetery between the youngest son and the fifth daughter of Christopher Betts Johnson senior. An examination of the six headstones at the graves of the Johnson family in the cemetery at Wortwell Chapel makes it clear there were father and son who had the same names and both were millers.

Joseph Stammers took over the mill around 1855 [21] or maybe earlier. He rented the mill and in 1861 he was paying a rental of £110 per annum (payable quarterly) for the mill, mill house, cottage, extensive outbuildings, gardens and meadowland, in all about seven acres (exclusive of water).[22] He was under an Agreement to quit at Michaelmas 1862 but obviously continued beyond that date as was evidenced in his Will. Indeed, Harrod & Co's Trade Directory of 1864, under Mendham, lists Joseph Stammers as a "miller, merchant and farmer".

A very detailed, exacting and lengthy Will was executed by Joseph Stammers and dated the 19th May 1863 together with a Codicil dated the 19th May 1864. He appointed his brother Robert, who was also a miller, of Gressenhall, Norfolk, William Leedes Fox, Gentleman of Harleston, Norfolk, and William Beverley Ringer, farmer of Mendham, Suffolk, as his executors and to them he left "Nineteen Guineas (£19 19s. 0d. or £19.95) each as some acknowledge-ment of the trouble they will be put to". He bequeathed all his household goods and effects to his wife Harriett, including "wines liquors and housekeep-ing provisions" together with the sum of £100. By his Will all his freehold property was vested in his Executors as Trustees "and also the machinery going gears apparatus and appendages in and about my Water Mill now occupied by me with their respective rights members and appurtenances". The Trustees were directed to "pay the rents issues and profits" to his wife during her life and "after her decease upon trust with all convenient speed to make sale and dispose of the same either together or in parcels and by public auction or private contract ....". The same directions applied to his copyhold property and the Trustees could, at their discretion, during his wife's lifetime dispose of his interest in any of his "copyhold or customary hereditaments" with monies arising from any sale or sales forming part of his residuary personal estate. His Will also laid down how his executors should deal with the farm he leased from Benjamin Charles Chaston both during his wife's lifetime and after her decease. After the usual testamentary expenses all money, personal estate and effects after conversion to money, had to be invested with the income paid to his wife. There were further directions as to how the interest from trust money should be dealt with after his wife's death. The Will discloses, inter alia, that Joseph Stammers was Harriett's second husband and that he had three brothers; also that William Leedes Fox was also his "Attorney and Solicitor". One of the two witnesses to the Will was a John Manning, Miller, of Mendham. The Codicil is witnessed by John Candler, Surgeon, Harleston and John Miller, Miller, Mendham.

Joseph Stammers died on the 10th July 1864 and his Will and Codicil were proved in the District Registry of the Court of Probate at Ipswich on the 24th August 1864.

On Wednesday 21st August 1861, the property was offered for sale by auction by Messrs. Lenny & Durrant at the Magpie Inn, Harleston, on instructions from the Executors of the late John Norman.

The Auctioneers' Sale Particulars describe the mill as "Now in Full Trade" and that it consists of "A very superior Water Corn Mill". Remembering that the mill was offered for sale at this time before it was enlarged the details of the mill contained in the Sale Particulars are interesting and informative.

The four floors are described as spacious and afford "stowage for upwards of thirty-five Lasts of corn, (i.e. about 73 tons)* besides flour, Pollard, and other Offals". The water wheel was stated to be "nearly 13ft 6ins in diameter" and that it had recently been fitted with a "capital timber shaft; and that the Pit Wheel, of corresponding dimensions, will be included in the Purchase of the Mill"! The mill was stated to have "Four pairs of French Burr Stones, Flour Machine, Jumper, and other machinery and going Gears complete". The fall of water was then "about five feet, and the power and capabilities of the entire property will bear a fair comparison with any other of a similar description in the counties of Suffolk and Norfolk".

It appears that George Chase purchased the mill property and he is cited in the Trade Directories as a miller and farmer at Mendham in 1865–1869.[23] When the mill was enlarged not only did George Chase instal the beam engine and the steam boiler but also a further four pairs of stones were fitted making a total of eight pairs.[24] (Rex Wailes in his "Suffolk Watermills", in Appendix A, says the mill had nine pairs of stones but elsewhere he mentioned it had eight pairs in 1887. However, the auction sale advertisement of 1887 states the mill was "driving nine pairs of stones".)

In 1872 John Munnings came to Mendham and joined George Chase in partnership.[25] John Munnings, who was one of nine children, had served his apprenticeship with his cousin Jeremiah Stannard at Nayland Mills, Essex, and was there for 18 years from 1854.[26] From 1872 onwards the firm was known as Chase & Munnings.[27]

In 1875 John Munnings married Ellen Emily Ringer of Walsham Hall, Mendham. It was said he courted her for no less than nine years and she, presumably tired of waiting, went to stay with her aunts at Southsea. John

* See footnote on page 20.

followed her and married her there. They had four sons, all born at the Mill House (see the Munnings Family Tree on page 83). The eldest, William Green, was a farmer. The next, Alfred James, was the famous artist who was President of the Royal Academy and a K.C.V.O. The third son, Frederick William, eventually took over the mill whilst the youngest son, Charles Edward, went to South Africa.[28]

In 1887 tragedy struck the partnership of Chase & Munnings. George Chase was thrown from his dogcart whilst in Harleston and was killed.[29] George Chase was obviously a successful miller and farmer owning a considerable amount of agricultural and other property. After his death his various properties were offered for sale, the particulars of which were as follows:—

PARTICULARS OF THE REAL ESTATE [30]
OF THE
LATE MR. GEORGE CHASE
For Sale by Auction
AT THE "MAGPIE" HOTEL, HARLESTON,
On Wednesday, the 29th of June, 1887
AT TWO FOR THREE O'CLOCK IN THE AFTERNOON
IN 14 LOTS

Hazard & Pratt,
Vendors' Solicitors
Harleston, Norfolk.

Geo. Durrant & Sons,
Auctioneers,
Redenhall Grange,
Harleston,
and Beccles.

LOT 1

DRANE'S FARM   In Weybread
A WELL-BUILT POST WINDMILL

on Brick Round House, very conveniently situated near the road, and standing well for wind and trade, fitted with Patent Sails and Self-winding Tackle, having Six floors, driving two pairs of Stones by wind, and two by steam, Flour Mill, Engine House, Malt Store, and Counting House, in the occupation of Messrs. Algar and Doggett, yearly tenants, at the annual rent of £40.

THE KILN HOUSE, THE BRICK YARDS, THE OLD KILN, DWELLINGHOUSE, PITT'S FARM HOUSE, A WELL-BUILT BRICK AND TILED COTTAGE.
The whole estate contains 153A. 3R. 39P.

LOT 2   In Weybread POPPY'S FARM 75A. OR. 14P.

LOT 3   In Weybread Small FARM 49A. OR. 34P.

LOT 4   In Weybread and Syleham LEFTLEY'S FARM 100A. 3R. 20P.

LOT 5   "POTASH MEADOWS" 20A. 1R. 4P., In Weybread.

LOT 6   In Weybread GOOD LOW MEADOWS 30A. OR. 4P.

LOT 7   DO. Brick & Tiled Double Cottage 1R. 25P.

LOT 8   In Linstead Magna SMALL FARM 38A. 2R. 11P.

LOT 9   IN MENDHAM, SUFFOLK
           about two miles from Harleston
           THE FOUR STOREY BRICK, BOARDED, AND TILED
           Steam and Water Power Flour Mills

NOW IN FULL TRADE, and capable of turning out between 400 and 500 Sacks of Flour per week,* DRIVING NINE PAIRS OF STONES (two pairs of which belong to the tenants) with WROUGHT IRON WATER WHEEL, and a 25-HORSE POWER HIGH AND LOW PRESSURE STEAM ENGINE by Holmes and Sons, Offal House with Chamber over, Engine Boiler and Coal Houses, Double Flood Gates, Brick Eel Tank, and Boat House.

A RANGE OF BRICK AND TILE BUILDINGS, comprising spacious Gig House, a four-stall Riding Horse Stable, Six Loose Boxes for Trade Horses with Straw Loft over, Chaff Cutting and Hay Houses, brick Dirt Bin, Piggeries, a Brick and Tiled 5-bayed Cart Lodge and two Loose Boxes.

ALSO THE BRICK AND TILED FAMILY RESIDENCE containing Entrance Hall, Dining Room with two closets, Drawing Room with folding doors opening to Garden and Office, Kitchen, Larder, Back Kitchen, Store Room, Six Bedrooms, and Spare Chamber.
Paved Court Yard, Coal, Wood, and Knife Houses, Pump, W.C., and well-fitted Office adjoining the Residence. Neat Flower Garden and Good Vegetable Garden, in the occupation of Messrs. Chase & Munnings.

Also included in Lot 9 —

*i.e. 50 to 62$\frac{1}{2}$ tons, assuming a sack contains 280lbs of flour.

"Waveney Cottages" newly built brick and tiled and near the Mill, in the occupation of Miss Beaumont, Samuel Notley, and James Souter, yearly Tenants at rents amounting to £15.

3 enclosures of fine Pasture Land in the occupation of Messrs. Chase & Munnings, containing together 6A. 3R. 20P. Freehold.

Possession of Lot 9 except cottages at Michaelmas next.

The Purchaser of this Lot shall in addition to his purchase-money pay the sum of £1,102. 4s. 0d. for all the LANDLORD'S MACHINERY AND FIXTURES in and about the Mill and premises, which have been recently valued by Messrs. Holmes and Sons of Norwich, and an Inventory of which will be produced at the Sale.

An Inventory of the Tenant's Fixtures, Machinery and Effects in and about the Mill and premises will also be produced at the Sale, and the purchaser will have the option of taking the same at Michaelmas by Valuation in the usual manner.

LOT 10   In Mendham Brick & Tiled Double Cottage in occupation of Arthur Saxby and Richard Palmer, yearly tenants at rents amounting to £8.

Also 3 enclosures of Arable and Pasture Land in the occupation of Messrs. Chase & Munnings 6A. 3R. 15P.

LOT 11   In Mendham Brick and Tiled Double Cottage Occupation Robert Self Yearly Rent £4.

LOT 12   In Mendham Brick and Tiled Double Cottage Occupation George Self Yearly Rent £3. 18s.

LOT 13   In Broome, Norfolk
          Family Mansion. "BROOME PLACE" Gardens and Grounds 20A. 3R. 10P. Vacant Possession.

LOT 14   Brick and Tiled House with shop and Bake Office
          Occupation John Saunders Yearly Rent £7.

Also 3 cottages occupation Mrs. Cullum, James Smith and Wm. Catchpole. Yearly Rents amounting to £8. 19s.

An advertisement relating to this sale appeared in "The Miller" dated 6th June 1887, and reads as follows:—

"To be sold at auction at the Magpie Hotel, Harleston, on June 29, the four storey, brick, boarded and tiled steam and water power flour mills situated at Mendham, Suffolk, now in full trade driving 9 pairs of stones, with wrought iron Water wheel and a 25 h.p. high and low pressure steam engine, by Holmes & Sons, offal house with chamber over, engine, boiler and coal houses. Also a range of buildings comprising gig house stables etc. and the family residence and offices, in the occupation of Messrs. Chase and Munnings."

It is to be noted that in the above details relating to the Mill, nine pairs of stones are mentioned. It therefore would appear that George Chase probably added a further five pairs to the original four pairs which were mentioned in the sale particulars of 1861.

After the death of George Chase, the mill became the property of the Revd E. C. Hopper of Starston[31] so presumably he bought Lot 9 at auction.

The Revd Edmund Carles Hopper, M.A. was Rector of Starston (which is about 3 miles from Mendham) from 1887 until 1922. He was the son of the Venerable Archdeacon Augustus M. Hopper, M.A., who was also Rector of Starston from 1845 until 1878. The Hoppers, who were also Patrons of the Living, gave a total of no less than 68 years service to the Parish.

John Munnings then kept the mill on, continuing as the tenant of the Revd E. C. Hopper, and fitted a $1\frac{1}{2}$ sack Turner Roller Plant keeping four of the eight pairs of stones.[32] Later, in 1905, he fitted a complete 3 sack Turner Roller Plant.[33]

In fact in October 1905 Mendham Mills were re-started after the complete refit by Messrs. E. R. & F. Turner of Ipswich and the announcement also states that the mills "have been carried on since 1872 by Mr. John Munnings". At the same time advantage was also taken of the occasion to give an entertainment at the mill in honour of the marriage of Mr. W. G. Munnings,[34] John's eldest son who eventually occupied and ran the mill. Quite when the mill became the property of the Munnings family is not known. After the death of the Revd Hopper, which occurred on the 7th June 1922, the mill then passed to one of his relatives. However, the mill was in the ownership of Frederick William Munnings at some stage because it was he who disposed of it in 1938.

In 1906, the equipment of the mill included a main driving shaft alongside a line of elevators and power from the water wheel or the engine was transmitted to the main shaft by a number of belts. The water wheel and engine could be used separately, or in combination. Apparently the water wheel was generally used except when the water was low then the engine was brought into use. On the first floor were to be found a line of Turner double roller mills and on the second floor, i.e. the top one, the remainder of the plant. A Turner double dustless machine effected purification and dressing; dusting and grading was done by centrifugals and reels.

John Munnings ground either all English wheat or a mixture of the best quality English available and a strong foreign kind, such as No. 1 Hard Manitoba. These wheats were generally clean and although an elaborate cleaning plant was not exactly essential, he ensured a pure grist by the use of an "Eureka" cleaning machine which thoroughly sifted, scoured and aspirated the wheat.[35]

Undoubtedly the mill was a successful and thriving business. Flour was carted from the mill to Bungay Staithe (usually by a Dennis lorry which had hard tyres) from whence it was taken by wherry to Yarmouth and then shipped to London and Newcastle.[36]

John Munnings was not only a successful miller, he was also a person not lacking in enterprise as the report in "The Miller" dated 3rd April 1911 will illustrate:

"Stone System Revival

Mr. John Munnings, of Mendham Mills, in Suffolk, has revived the stone system of flour making, and last month was "at home" at his mills to all the people of the district, who had received invitations to come and see the process of manufacturing and then take a cup of tea at the mill house. This enterprising move was well supported. While the booming of the so called standard flour has not the active support of many millers, it has had some unexpected results in stirring up enterprise that had been lying dormant in many of our country millers, who have been stimulated to more vigorous efforts in various directions to capture a trade, which, however, is not likely to last."

On 22nd July 1905 John Munnings executed his Will. This was a short and concise document in which he bequeathed all his real and personal estate "whatsoever and wheresoever" to his wife Ellen whom he appointed his Sole Executrix.[37] He was then aged 66. He died in early 1914 aged 75 and on the 4th April 1914 his wife was granted probate of his Will at Ipswich.[37]

John Munnings, apart from being a well-known miller in the area, certainly entered into the life of the village. It seems he was quite a religiously minded fellow and attended All Saints Church, Mendham, regularly where he usually read a lesson, and clearly he is the kind of person who would have been a Churchwarden. The Parish Church records for the period in question could not be consulted as they had been destroyed by a certain Incumbent! However, he is listed as a Churchwarden in the records of the Archdeaconry of Suffolk for 1892.[38] John was chairman of the Village School Governors — probably the first. In common with other towns and villages Mendham celebrated Queen Victoria's Diamond Jubilee in 1897 and John Munnings was elected Hon. Secretary at the inaugural meeting of the Celebrations Committee held in the Board School Room on 9th May 1897. From the Minute Book, which he kept, interesting details can be gleaned. Among several matters discussed John Munnings proposed the bell ringers be paid thirty shillings to officiate during the day and to ring hand bells after the dinner; also there be a distribution of Jubilee medals to the children. He was subsequently instructed to procure 240 such medals and "a sixpenny one for each of the Committee". John was one of the many subscribers to the celebration fund, donating £2, another being the celebrated Revd Dr. J. J. Raven. Later in the Committee's proceedings John also acted as Treasurer taking over from the person originally appointed. Later, at the King Edward VII Coronation celebrations of 1902, John's eldest son, William Green Munnings, was elected Hon. Secretary of that Committee. The Sports Committee for these celebrations included W.G. Munnings and his brother A.J. Munnings, the artist.

Following John's death the milling business was carried on for a short while by his widow because in Kelly's Trade Directory of 1916 there is an entry "Mrs. Ellen Emily Munnings, Mendham Roller Mills (Frederick Wm. Munnings, Manager), Mendham, Harleston". Eventually Frederick William Munnings took over the mill, he certainly had done so by 1922, when he was using steam and water power. At the same time he was in business as a cartage contractor.[39] Incidentally, William married his cousin Ellen Ringer who was known as Nellie. (See the Family Tree on page 83).

During Frederick Munnings' occupation of the mill, the Holmes 25 h.p. Beam Engine was removed during the Autumn of 1923.[40] It was driven for over 50 years by Mr. James Souter ("Jimmy") and it is said that he was so attached to "his" engine, it being his life, that when it was dismantled he died of a broken heart. As the engine driver, James, would not allow anyone to attend the engine or to interfere with it. Furthermore he never experienced a breakdown with his engine.[41] The reason for the removal of the Beam Engine was because it had virtually worn out and it was difficult to obtain spare parts. The Beam Engine was replaced by a Lister Diesel Engine and later the Lister was replaced by a Ruston-Hornsby Engine. There was a generator for electricity which was driven by water power and electricity was installed on 20th December 1923. All these changes were carried out by Frederick Munnings.[42]

In 1931, by a Deed of Assignment dated the 30th June, Frederick Wm. Munnings sold "the goodwill of the business of a flour miller" to Messrs. Smith & Son (Langley Mill) Limited whose registered office was at Langley Mill in the County of Nottingham. But the Assignment did not include "any Part of the goodwill of the Vendor in his said business of provender milling or in any business other than the milling of flour hereby assigned". This meant that Frederick Munnings could not "at any time hereafter either solely or jointly with or as managing Director or Agent for any other person or company directly or indirectly carry on or be engaged or concerned or interested in any part of England or Wales south of a line drawn from Aberystwyth to Birmingham, from Birmingham to Goole and from Goole to the mouth of the River Humber (including in the prohibited area any town through which such line passes) in the business or manufacturing or selling of flour or in any business competing with the business of the goodwill whereof is hereby assigned". He was not prevented from "acting as a corn merchant, Grist Miller and/or as Flour Factor or Agent in the purchase or selling of Flour . . ."

The area to which these restrictive covenants applied was more than half of England and Wales and it is somewhat difficult to understand or appreciate just why Frederick Munnings was precluded from milling flour in such a vast area. It seems extraordinary that a comparatively modest country miller should be bound so strictly in such a matter. Quite why he agreed to comply with the Purchasers' requests is not known except of course he received a consideration for entering into the agreement and this amounted to £1,258 10s. 0d. He further agreed to "remove from the said Mills and premises all the plant and machinery therein used exclusively in connection with the milling of flour or shall at the option of the Vendor to the reasonable satisfaction of the Purchaser carry out therein such alterations as may preclude the use thereof for the purpose of milling flour".

Frederick Munnings was well and truly tied up. Furthermore these restrictive covenants were attached to the premises and "any buildings or erections at any time thereon" which means any future purchasers of the premises have to observe such covenants.

Frederick Munnings carried on as a Provender Miller until he sold the property on the 29th July 1938 to Grace Mary Philcox for £1,600. The purchaser then converted part of the mill into residential accommodation thus extending that of the Mill House. At the time the mill "was completely stripped down to the frame, infilled with fire proof bricks, plastered then totally re-clad in seasoned timber and painted".[43] It had £20,000 spent on it[44] — a very considerable sum in those pre-war days.

It is understood that the water wheel (which remains in situ in a dilapidated condition, together with the pitwheel and certain gearing), worked from the date of conversion to living accommodation until 1949. It is also understood there was no main electricity in the village of Mendham until the early 1950's, when the Water Board provided the mill with mains electricity, i.e. they paid the Electricity Authority to take the supply to the mill in exchange for giving up the right to abstract water from the river.

More recently the property was offered for sale by private treaty in 1985, by

Messrs. Savills of Norwich, offers being invited in the region of £280,000 for the freehold as a whole, i.e. the mill and mill house, out-buildings, Waveney Cottage, mill cottage, School Paddock and Old Vicarage Paddock, in all about 22 acres, as Lot 1, or the Mill, Mill House, out-buildings, and about 13 acres as Lot 2 for which offers in the region of £175,000 were invited, the remainder being offered in four further lots. The property was in fact disposed of in separate lots and not as a whole.

In January 1988 the property was again on offer, this time by Prudential Property Services of Norwich, at an asking price of £345,000 for the mill, mill house, out-buildings, trout farm and about 13 acres. It is understood that it was sold to Newby Developments Limited of Ipswich for a figure in excess of the asking price. Two Planning Applications were submitted for approval, the first to upgrade the miller's house for separate occupation, to convert the annexe into a home and to relocate the trout fishery office; the second application was to convert the Coach House to two houses. In spite of several objections and Water Officials's warnings that the narrow access road was subject to flooding, approval was granted to both applications.

The Miller's House has been completely renovated and was offered for sale in December 1991 at £98,500. At the same time the Old Coach House was offered for sale at £75,000 with planning permission for conversion into either one or two houses, some major works having been carried out.

Mendham Watermill and the Mill House are both Listed Buildings Grade II under the Town & Country Planning Acts. They are both privately owned and not open to the public.

MENDHAM WATERMILL

1.   Blomefield's "History of Norfolk", 1806, Vol.V, p.372.
2.   Proceedings of Parliament 1523.
3.   Ibid.
4.   S.R.O. (I) HA12/B4/29/83.
5.   Rex Wailes, "Suffolk Watermills", Excerpts Transactions of the Newcomen Society, 1964–1965, p.110.
6.   John Munnings, "The Passing of the Country Miller and his Mill, River Stour and Waveney", unpublished article, c. 1970.
7.   Rex Wailes, Op. Cit. p.106.
8.   "Milling", December 22nd 1906, p.759.
9.   Ibid.
10. Mrs. Kathleen Hadingham (née Munnings), sketch and information in her possession.
11. London Gazette, September 26–29, 1807.
12. Norfolk Chronicle, December 26, 1807.

13. London Gazette, March 11–14, 1809.
14. Ipswich Journal, September 11, 1813.
15. Ipswich Journal, December 4, 1813.
16. Mrs. Kathleen Hadingham Op.Cit., copy of Deed plan, inscribed, "The property of Mr. Norman".
17. London Gazette, January 18, 1814.
18. Ipswich Journal, March 30, 1830.
19. White's Directory, 1844.
20. London Gazette, January 25, 1853.
21. White's Directory, 1855.
22. Messrs. Lenny & Durrant's Auction Sale Particulars, 1861.
23. Kelly's Directories 1865 and 1869.
24. John Munnings, Op.Cit.
25. Mrs. Kathleen Hadingham, Op. Cit.
26. John Munnings, Op.Cit.
27. Ibid.
28. Mrs. Kathleen Hadingham, Op.Cit.
29. John Munnings, Op.Cit.
30. S.R.O. (I) HB26: 412/1626.
31. "Milling", Op.Cit.
32. John Munnings, Op.Cit., and Rex Wailes, Op.Cit., p105.
33. John Munnings, Op.Cit.
34. "The Miller", November 6, 1905.
35. "Milling", Op.Cit.
36. John Munnings, Op.Cit.
37. S.R.O. (I) IC/AA2/184 137 3 Folios.
38. S.R.O. (I) FAA/30/49/1.
39. Kelly's Directory, 1922.
40. Mrs. Kathleen Hadingham, Op.Cit.
41. "Milling", Op.Cit.
42. Mrs. Kathleen Hadingham, Op.Cit.
43. Savills, Estate Agents, Norwich, Sale Particulars, c.1985.
44. Sir Alfred Munnings, KCVO, PPRA, "The Finish", 1952, p.299.

THE MUNNINGS FAMILY

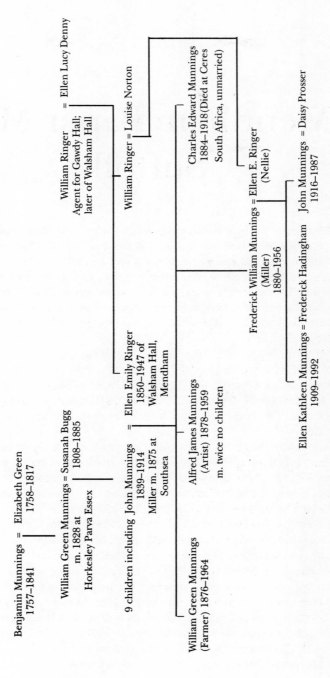

Benjamin Munnings = Elizabeth Green
1757–1841   1758–1817

William Green Munnings = Susanah Bugg
m. 1828 at   1808–1885
Horkesley Parva Essex

9 children including John Munnings = Ellen Emily Ringer
1839–1914   1850–1947 of
Miller m. 1875 at   Walsham Hall,
Southsea   Mendham

William Green Munnings
(Farmer) 1876–1964

Alfred James Munnings
(Artist) 1878–1959
m. twice no children

Frederick William Munnings = Ellen E. Ringer
(Miller)   (Nellie)
1880–1956

William Ringer
Agent for Gawdy Hall;
later of Walsham Hall

William Ringer = Louise Norton

Charles Edward Munnings
1884–1918 (Died at Ceres
South Africa, unmarried)

William Ringer = Ellen Lucy Denny

John Munnings = Daisy Prosser
1916–1987

Ellen Kathleen Munnings = Frederick Hadingham
1909–1992

I am indebted to the late Mrs. E. Kathleen Hadingham for this information on her family.

Mendham Paper Mill, Suffolk

John Munnings states in his unpublished article "The Passing of the Country Miller and his Mill, Rivers Stour and Waveney, "c. 1970, "There was once a paper mill on the old river near Mendham Church".

This is quite a definite statement but unfortunately he does not elaborate and no details or authority are given. The writer was unable to speak with John Munnings on this or other matters relating to the Watermills because of his being incapacitated through illness over a long period. Sadly he died on the 12th November 1987.

No papermill appears in Mendham on Hodskinson's Map of 1783, Bryant's Map of 1797 or Bryant's Map of 1824/25.

Shorter in his standard work entitled "Paper Mills and Paper Makers in England 1495–1800" at pages 217, 218 and 219 mentions ten paper mills in Norfolk and five in Suffolk which includes Bungay but Mendham is not mentioned.

Having made enquiries of various local persons, Mr. Fred Hadingham of Mendham says the paper mill was probably on the Mendham Drain (presumably the "old river" mentioned by John Munnings) opposite (but more likely at or adjoining) the then thatched cottage which has recently been replaced by a modern bungalow. (This is the first bungalow on the left as one enters the village from the Wortwell Road via the iron bridge). If it did exist, this mill would have been some 120 yards north of the Church. There does not appear to be any conclusive evidence that a paper mill existed at Mendham. On the other hand, the fact that no record of such a mill seems to be available is not necessarily proof of its non-existence. Clearly further research is required.

However, the writer is of the opinion that John Munnings may possibly have made his statement as a result of the corn mill at Mendham being advertised for sale in December 1813 and described as being "well adapted for corn or paper mills". If this premise is correct then there was not a separate or another mill at Mendham used for the production of paper.

Limbourne Watermill, Wortwell, 1988. D F Pluck.

Limbourne Watermill, Wortwell, 1988. Showing pitwheel, wallower and great spurwheel. D F Pluck.

Limbourne Watermill, Wortwell, Suffolk

NGR TM282844

At the time of the Domesday Survey a mill existed at "Linburna". "Saint Edmund, that is, Bury Abbey, held thirty acres of land in Linburn, with five bordars, or labourers, two acres of meadow, and a fifth part of a mill: the whole was worth 10s., but it expressly stated that the Bishop of Thetford had soc and sac." (The right of holding a local court).[1]

The following quotation tends to indicate the relative importance locally of Limbourne mill "Kirby says, there are but few or no tenants belonging to this manor, and it would scarce be known, if it were not for the water-mill, which still retains the name of Limber Mill. This mill was sold some years since to Aldous Arnold, of Lowestoft, Esq., and is at present the property of the Rev. Richard Aldous Arnold, Rector of Ellough (c.1830)."[2]

"The manor of Limbourne in Homersfield, formerly belonged to the Nuns of Bungay."[3] This was a Benedictine Nunnery and since most Benedictine Abbeys and Priories were founded around 1100, it is reasonable to assume that the manor existed before that era and, as was usual, a mill or mills formed part of the manor's attributes. In any event, Wortwell is mentioned in the Domesday Survey. Unfortunately little is known of this particular manor but there were freehold lands known as "Limber Lands" and "Limber Mill" in the parish. Much later these, together with Downs Farm, were purchased by Alexander Adair of Flixton Hall.[4]

A conveyance dated "Monday after St. Ambrose, 8 Edward III" (11th April 1334), of the manor of Gyllyngham, Flixton and Sancroft and advowson of the Church of Gyllyngham also includes two water mills called Lymburgh Mills.[5] In 1356 (12th April 30 Edward III) a conveyance of the manor of Flixton includes a mill and meadow Lymbone and appurtenances.[6] Also another conveyance dated "Monday after St. Ambrose 38 Edward III" (8th April 1364) of the manor of Gyllyngham, Flixton and Sancroft and advowson of the Church of Gyllyngham again includes two water mills called Lymburghmilles.[7] This is followed by a lease of this property dated "Inv. H.C. 38 Edward III" (3rd

May 1364), which also includes the two water mills called Lymburghmilles.[8]

It is suggested that the two "Lymburghmilles" are in effect Limbourne Mill, Wortwell, which at that time had two pairs of stones under the one roof. The village of Wortwell lies to the west of "The Saints", i.e. the seven hamlets of South Elmham, and they are: St. Mary otherwise Homersfield, St. Cross or Sancroft St. George, St. Margaret, St. James, All Saints-cum-St. Nicholas, St. Peter, St. Michael. The manor of Sancroft mentioned in the 14th century documents would seem to tie up with South Elmham St. Cross.

In 1762, and quite likely at sometime earlier, the occupier of Limbourne Mill or Mills was one Stephen Stannard. He was obviously a tenant because his father-in-law, John Moore who was a tow-dresser,* was the owner of the mill. In 1762 John Moore was ailing in health and so on the 20th May 1762 he executed his last Will and Testament "being week and Infirm in body but of sound Mind Memory and Understanding". In his Will he left to his son-in-law, Stephen Stannard, "All that my Mefsuage or Tenement wherein I now Dwell . . . Situate and Lying in Homersfield aforesaid And also all that my Water Grist Mill & Mills & Hemp Bunching Mill (being under One Roof) commonly Called or known by the name of Limborn Mill or Mills with the Appurtenances in the Parish of Homersfield . . ." The bequest was to Stephen Stannard "and his assigns for the term of Two Years from and after my Decease and no longer and Immediately after the Expiration of the said Term of Two Years or in Case of his Death which shall first happen Then I Give Devise and Bequeath All and Singular aforesaid Premifses with their and every of their Appurtenances unto my Grandson Stephen Stannard (son of the above named Stephen Stannard) and to his Heirs and Afsigns for ever . ." The premises also stood liable and subject to the " Payment of one clear Annuity or Rent Charge of Six Pounds" to John Moore's daughter, Sarah the wife of Stephen Stannard, and during the Term of her natural Life by half-yearly payments. He left all his household goods, furniture and chattels to his grandson Stephen Stannard. For a reason best known to himself, John Moore bequeathed to his son John Moore "the sum of Twenty Shillings only to be paid by my Son in Law Stephen Stannard within One Month next after my Decease"![9]

By 1767 the occupier of the Mill or Mills was William Titshall when the premises were offered for sale, presumably on instructions from the grandson Stephen Stannard, as indicated by the following advertisement which appeared in the Ipswich Journal of August 26th 1767:

* Tow — Coarse and broken fibres of flax or hemp separated by Heckling and ready for spinning.

'To be SOLD, and entered upon at Michaelmas next O.S. An ancient and well-accuftom'd WATER-MILL, with a Bunching-Mill for Hemp adjoining, with a Dwelling-houfe and other Outhoufes, and about two Acres of Meadow-Land adjoining to the faid Mill and Houfe, with Commonage on Limborn Common; the whole being in tolerable Repair, and all Freehold fituated in the Parifh of HOMERSFIELD in the County of Suffolk, known or called by the Name of Limborn Mill, within 3 Miles of Harlefton in Norfolk, and about four Miles of Bungay in Suffolk; two very good Market-Towns.

For Particulars enquire of Mr. Thomas Goode, Cooper, at Wortwell, Norfolk; or of Mr. Wm. Titfhall, the prefent Occupier; who will fhew the Premifes.'

When inspecting the interior of the mill some interesting carvings in the timbers were observed. On the ground floor in a wood bracket of the framing is carved a fleur-de-lis beneath which CS 1783 (or possibly 1785) and RS again with a date in the 1780's, the last digit being unclear. On another ground floor bracket W + V 1783 and E + H 97 is carved, while on a top floor beam J NURSEY and JB (or possibly JR) can be seen.

It is difficult to suggest what these letters or initials and dates refer to. They could well have been carved by men who worked in the mill or by those engaged in building operations. They remain a tantalising mystery.

This mill was known as "Limber Mill" in 1824 and 1826 and is shown as such on Bryant's maps of these dates; also as such on the Ordnance Survey 6 inch map of the latter date. On the first edition of the Ordnance Survey 1 inch map, the mill is named Limbourne Mill. The mill is also indicated on the earlier maps of 1736 (Kirby's) and 1760 (Bowen's).

In 1822 Edward Hill was the miller[10] and he remained certainly until 1836.[11] A Commission of Bankrupt dated 24th December 1825, was announced against "Robert Crytoft Harvey, of Alburgh, County of Norfolk, and Edward Hill of Wortwell, Said County, Millers and Flour Merchants. Accounts to be audited." [12] Later, in 1830, a further announcement by the Commission of Bankrupt against the "co-partners" indicated, "Harvey to be issued certificate 5 Nov."[13] Edward Hill himself may have satisfied his creditors because he seems to have continued at Limbourne Mill until well into 1838, in fact up to September of that year.[14]

By 1850 William Tippell is cited as the miller at Wortwell,[15] and in 1854 and 1855 Christopher Johnson* appears;[16] also in 1858.[17] Richard Doggett, a

*See notes on Mendham Mill, page 71.

farmer who resided at Hall Farm, Wortwell (close by the mill) is shown as the miller in 1865,[18] 1868,[19] and 1869.[20]

An invoice dated the 9th of August 1872 shows Samuel Goulder to be the miller when 10 stones of flour were sold to Robert Todd of Wortwell for £1 3s 4d.

Samuel was still the miller when the property was offered for public auction on the 22nd of August 1878 by Mr. Henry Read at the Public Hall, Lowestoft. Lot 19 was described as "A Highly Desirable Farm and Water Mill". It included a residence known as Wortwell Hall, a set of agricultural buildings, a watermill, known locally as Limbourne Mill "driving three pairs of French Burr Stones", an attached double millers cottage, a granary and cart-shed. The land consisted of arable and meadow land extending altogether to 177 acres, 1 rood and 30 perches. It is interesting to note that the conditions of sale referred to purchase deeds dated the 4th and 5th October 1768 and 21st and 22nd May 1783 and an indenture dated 10th and 11th January 1803 as to various parts of Lot 19. The auction sale particulars are marked in pencil against this Lot "£6,000 bid by Holmes withdrawn". Obviously bidding did not reach the reserve price and the property therefore did not sell at auction.

Harry Goulder, farmer of Wortwell Hall, was operating the mill one year later in 1879.[21] By 1883 Phillip Goulder was the miller and he continued at least until 1892.[22] By 1900, Robert James Smith, who also farmed at Says Farm, is tenant of the mill.[23] He remained as tenant until July 1910 when he bought the mill at auction for the sum of £500[24] and then continued as miller right through until 1933.[25] Until the 1930's the mill had a small roller plant of about $1/2$ sack capacity.[26] On the death of R.J. Smith the mill was acquired by Brian I. Marriage[27] who also owned Pakenham Watermill which stands on a tributary stream of the river Blackbourne 6 miles north-east of Bury St. Edmunds. Pakenham Watermill has been restored to working order and is open to the public on certain days.

Limbourne ceased as a working mill some time prior to 1949 when it was purchased by Mr. Arthur Henry Bush Jnr., of the Magpie Hotel, Harleston from the previous owner, an artist by the name of Smith. Mr. Bush, whose father had owned and operated Needham Watermill, had hired the water by the mill before he bought it. He caught many hundredweights of eels which he sold to London hotels and restaurants. Incidentally, many Domesday mills paid rent partly in cash and partly in eels.

Mr. Bush died in 1973 and in consequence thereof, Wortwell Mill was again offered for sale by auction, this time by Messrs. Apthorpes at the Magpie Hotel, Harleston on instructions from the Executors of the late Mr. Bush. The sale took place on 26th September 1973. The particulars of sale describe the mill as "a unique property" and Mr. Arthur Bush was aptly described — "for nearly half a century the proprietor of the famous Magpie Hotel, Harleston, where he became an extremely well-known personality to people from far and wide as well as being a much respected figure throughout Norfolk and Suffolk." The sale particulars go on to say that "Limbourne Mill was the last corn mill on the River Waveney to cease operating on a trading basis. The River Waveney is renowned for silver eel which can be trapped at this point. Arthur Bush maintained traps here for very many years and claimed in one year to have caught as many as half a ton in weight of eels." Even when in his eighties he would assist in pulling in the eel net.[28]

In 1973 the mill and adjoining cottage was also described as being "listed on the supplementary list as being a building of special architectural or historic importance". In the sale room bidding started at £20,000 and finished at £47,000, the property being bought by Messrs. Thomas William Gaze of Diss for a client.

Little of the mill machinery remains. The external waterwheel is no longer in place although the cast-iron pitwheel on a cast-iron $10^1/_2$ inch diameter shaft remains. The pitwheel is in two sections, 7ft. 5ins. in diameter, with eight arms and 128 teeth. The cast-iron wallower with six arms and 54 teeth remains on a vertical cast-iron shaft of 7 to $7^1/_2$ ins. diameter where there is also a wooden pulley wheel with cast-iron compass arms for a belt drive to the tentering gear; the latter no longer exists. There are cast-iron bridge trees for supporting the stone nuts. The great spur wheel remains; it is of wood construction in five sections with 120 wooden teeth and six cast-iron arms. The crown wheel is also of wooden construction with wooden teeth in mesh with two cast-iron gear wheels which drove two layshafts, one having a large cast-iron pulley and a wooden grooved pulley for the sack hoist drive; the other having a cast-iron pulley. There is an outside pulley for connection to an auxiliary engine.

Limbourne Mill is an attractive building of timber framed construction on a brick base, the exterior being weather-boarded and white painted under a pantile covered roof. It has a lucam on the front elevation, also weather-boarded and pantiled. The cottage adjoins the mill at its south-eastern corner.

The mill is privately owned and used partly for residential and partly for storage purposes. It is a Listed Building Grade II under the Town & Country Planning Acts.

LIMBOURNE WATERMILL

1. The Rev. Alfred Suckling, LL.B., "The History and Antiquities of the County of Suffolk", Vol. I, 1846, P.213.
2. Ibid. p.214.
3. "Excursions in the County of Suffolk", Vol. II, 1891, p.101.
4. Augustus Page, "A Supplement to the Suffolk Traveller", 1844, p.338.
5. S.R.O. (I) HA/12/B1/4/41.

6. S.R.O. (I) HA/12/B2/2/15.
7. S.R.O. (I) HA/12/B2/8/18.
8. S.R.O. (I) HA/12/B2/3/27.
9. N.R.O. NCC Roper 38.
10. Pigot & Co.'s Directory.
11. White's Directory.
12. London Gazette, 21st March 1828.
13. London Gazette, 15th October 1830.
14. Bury Post, 10th September 1838.
15. White's Directory.
16. Hunt's Directory.
17. Post Office Directory.
18. Kelly's Directory.
19. J.G. Harrod's Directory.
20. Kelly's Directory.
21. Ibid.
22. Ibid.
23. Ibid.
24. "The Miller" 1st August 1910.
25. Kelly's Directory.
26. John Munnings, "The Passing of the Country Miller and his Mill, Rivers Stour and Waveney", Unpublished Article, c.1970.
27. Kelly's Directory.
28. Eastern Daily Press, 13th September 1973.

Homersfield Watermill, c. 1900. The person standing in the mill is believed to be Mr Albert Fisher of Wortwell. The man standing in the cart is thought to be Mr John Carter. Courtesy of Frank Honeywood.

Homersfield Watermill, post 1927. Showing the spur wheel (pitwheel) in mesh with smaller spur wheel on the end of the horizontal shaft on which are three large bevel wheels to drive the stone nuts. [After demolition.] Courtesy of Frank Honeywood.

Homersfield Watermill, Suffolk

NGR TM284854

(St. Mary South Elmham, otherwise Homersfield)

There was a mill here i.e. Humbresfelda, at the Domesday Survey and a mill is shown on the Suffolk maps of Kirby 1736, Bowen 1760 and Faden 1783, also on Bryant's map of 1824/5 but unnamed on the 1826 edition.

The last mill at Homersfield was built over the mill stream. It was a small mill constructed of the traditional timber framing, having external white painted weather-boarding under a pantile covered roof and a lucam built into the front slope of the roof. It had a covered external waterwheel, which was of timber construction with "straight paddles or buckets".[1] The mill's machinery arrangement was of bevel gears from a layshaft. As far as can be ascertained, it was the only mill on the Waveney with such a layout. It had a spur wheel instead of the more usual bevel wheel for a pitwheel, the latter being in mesh with a smaller spur wheel fitted at the end of a horizontal shaft running down the centre of the mill. On the horizontal shaft were three large bevel gear wheels to drive the stone nuts. There would therefore have been three pairs of stones. There was a further spur gear for driving the sack hoist and dressing machinery.[2] The mill ran "left-handed" or, as the old millers would say "widdershins". This was a bygone term indicating the stones were dressed "against the sun" or "left-handed".[3] Adjoining the mill at its north-eastern end was the mill cottage.

The Bishop of Norwich held a watermill at Homersfield in the 1320's and it was let for £4.6s.8d. a year. ('Mills of Medieval England', R. Holt, 1988).

There was a Quit Claim, i.e. a deed of release, relating to two messuages called Sancroft and Newehalle with advowson of the Church of Sancroft and two watermills, with lands, etc., in Southelmham, from William, son and heir of Robert de Barsham, to William Bateman, Southelmham, Monday after Palm Sunday, 46 Edward III (17 April 1372).[4] It is uncertain as to exactly which watermills are referred to in this document but it is suggested it could well be an early Homersfield mill that had two pairs of stones. On the other hand, if the reference is really to two separate mills, then there is a likelihood of it meaning two of the three mills in the immediate neighbourhood —Flixton, Limbourne and Homersfield. Unfortunately one cannot state with any degree of certainty on the evidence available as to which watermill or mills is or are referred to.

A manorial administration document of 24 Henry VI, (1444–1445), includes accounts for the repairs to Homesfield mill.[5] Also included in this document was the cost of building a mill at Homersfield, in the same period which amounted to £4 13s. $9^1/_2$d., including "dammyng". Rex Wailes quotes this information in his paper "Suffolk Watermills"[7] as well as the detailed items of repair, etc., for 1467–1468. Another such document of 7 Edward IV, (1467–1468)[6] includes accounts for new millstones and spindle for the mill and for repairing the mill and mill pond (Homersfield):-

New millstone at Yarmouth	53/4
Loading and cartage	3/4
Damming the pond 4 days at 4d.	1/4
New Spindle	2/7
Carting timber to the saw pit and to Homersfield Bridge	1/4
Sawing 2 men 10 days at 8d.	6/8
4 cart loads of straw at 1/8	6/8
Nails for weatherboards and laths	2

These repairs therefore amounted to £3 15s. 5d. (£3.77).

Again a manorial administration document of Michaelmas 9 Edward IV to Michaelmas 10 Edward IV (1469–1470) includes accounts for repairs to the mill and Homersfield bridge (Manor of Southelmham).[8]

Another interesting document mentions the mill in connection with a grant of fishing in the River Waveney from Blake Pool to Homersfield mill. The grant was made by John Tasburgh and his son John to Elizabeth Hollond for the term of the lives of the two Tasburghs at an annual rent of 4d. This was part of the fishing granted to the two Tasburghs for their lives by the Bishop and Chapter of Norwich, between Caldwell towards Lymborne to Stowefen in Bungay at an annual rent of 6 partridges and 2 pheasants or the sum of 2/-. The grant to Elizabeth Hollond is dated 30 Nov. 36 Henry VIII (1544).[9]

Homersfield mill appears to be included in a document dealing with the exemplification of property which embraced the manor of Southelmham with appurtenances, six messuages, one watermill, one dovecot, view of frankpledge, etc., and dated 1 July 1612.[10]

A Note dated 20 June 1655 exists concerning the "flote" at Homersfield which was from ancient times placed 10 rods (165 feet) from the mill at Homersfield, but because of the decayed state of the bank and the resulting floods which meant the miller could grind but little corn, it was removed at the request of Charles Tasburgh, Flixton, owner of the mill, to the common pasture of Alborough and Wortwell (Norfolk) with the consent of the inhabitants of Alborough and Wortwell as long as the flote should stay there.[11]

Robert Harvey was the miller at Homersfield Mill in 1776 and on the 12th March of that year he insured his household goods, in his dwellinghouse at Homersfield for £50 and the utensils and stock in trade in his Water Corn Mill for £150. Both house and mill were at that time thatched.[12]

An advertisement appeared in February 1830 for a journeyman miller wanted at Homersfield Mill.[13]

In 1844 David Green was the "corn miller" at Homersfield Mill.[14]

In 1848 John Aston (his name is spelt Asten in Trade Directories) rented the mill and land from Sir Robert Shafto Adair, Bart., from the 11th October from year to year at £80 per annum. The Articles of Agreement were as follows:-

"And the said John Aston, his Executors, Administrators or Assigns shall during the said term keep in good and tenantable repair the said Water Mill, Floats, Gates, Wheels, Coggs, running and going Gears, Dams, Banks, Flood-Gates, Sluices, Posts, Pales, Rails, Fences and Glass windows and the lead thereof being allowed rough timber for the reparation of the same And shall fetch all such Materials as shall be wanted for the repair of the said Premises during the term And shall and will Yield up at the termination of this Agreement the Said Water Mill in a going and working condition with one pair of stones at least in use he the said John Aston, his Executors, Administrators, or Assigns being allowed by the said Sir Robert Shafto Adair his Heirs or Assigns or by the incoming Tenant a reasonable and fair value or recompense for whatever addition shall have been made to the running and going gears mentioned in the Schedule annexed . . ."

"Schedule of the Machinery &c. belonging to Sir Robert Shafto Adair in Homersfield Mill
One pair of Mill Stones, Water Wheel and Shaft, Pit Wheel, Counter Wheel and Shaft, Wallower Nut, one Stone Nut, four Drums and Straps, One Jumper with all the brasses belonging to the above."

The Agreement was dated November 10th 1848 and later, was marked "Expired 11 October 1870 Tenant's Notice. Mr. C. Smith £100".[15]

So John Aston ran the mill for a total of 22 years and was immediately followed by Charles Smith at an increased rent.

In fact Charles Smith took a lease for a term of eight years, commencing at Michaelmas 1870 and expiring at Michaelmas 1878, at a yearly rent of £100. The lease was dated the 14th February 1871 and varied insofar as to certain conditions when compared with the agreement entered into by John Aston. The lease recited, inter alia:-

"Always reserved unto the Said landlord all game fish Rabbits and wild fowl . . . but the tenant is to be at liberty to use nets for the purpose of taking eels as usually done by Millers upon the Waveney Stream . . ." ". . . Charles Smith his Executors or administrators shall and will from time to time and at all times during this demise and at his and their own costs and charges keep and maintain the said mill and the going gears and machinery of and belonging thereto respectively belonging . . . bridges, water-courses Dykes and Drains." The Schedule of machinery belonging to the landlord, Sir Robert Alexander Shafto Adair, was similar to that included in the Agreement dated 10th November 1848.[16]

There were two further tenancy agreements in respect of the mill, house and land, both in favour of Charles Smith, dated 3rd July 1879 and 7th May 1900, respectively. The latter was drawn by Messrs. Nicholl Manisty & Co., of 1 Howard Street, Strand, W.C. The agreement was from Sir Hugh E. Adair, Bart., to Mr. Charles Smith and the property formed part of the Flixton Estate. The tenancy was "for one year from the 11th October 1899, and so on from year to year until it is determined at the end of the first or any subsequent year by either party giving to the other twelve months' notice in writing at the yearly rent of Sixty Pounds payable half-yearly on the 6th day of April and the 11th day of October in each year". Again the schedule of the machinery in and about the mill, being the property of the landlord, was similar as that mentioned in the previous agreements. The schedule of the property was:-

		1A	1R	10P
44	Mill Meadow	1A	1R	10P
45	House and Garden		1	17
50	Float Meadow	3	3	35
98	Suffolk Marsh	4		4
	A	9	2	26

The Agreement was signed by Charles Smith and witnessed by John Sillitt of Homersfield Mill.[17]

When Charles Smith, a bachelor, died on 13th June 1901, the mill (presumably the unexpired portion of his lease together with fixtures and fittings, etc., belonging to the tenant) was left to his niece, Miss R. Gower. She was still running the mill in 1912.[18] When Charles Smith occupied the mill he "purchased several Bakers Shops in the district and made his mill with the Bakers Shops a closed circle", so that it would appear he lived a few years before his time.[19]

In 1900 Charles Smith was described not only as a miller but as a landowner and Churchwarden.[20] Refreshment was provided at the mill by Charles Smith for the 1892 Rogation Perambulation.[21] Mr. Smith lived in Homersfield for the whole of his life of 75 years. He had been associated with the milling business at the mill, either as assistant or proprietor, for no less than 60 years — a veritable record.

Mr. H.W. Hadingham, farmer, had wheat ground for wholemeal flour as well as corn ground at Homersfield Mill during 1902, and, for a short while when he moved to Earsham Farm at Michaelmas 1910.

During the time Miss Gower ran the mill, a Mr. Nunn worked for her and delivered the wholemeal flour and ground corn by horse and cart.[22]

In 1916 and 1922, Messrs. Woods, Sadd, Moore & Co. Ltd., of 12 Thorpe Road, Norwich, are listed as operating the "steam roller mills, Loddon; Lowestoft; Yarmouth; Homersfield and Trefoil Mill Harleston, Steam".[23]

The cessation of mill operations at Homersfield Mill was not due to a fire but came about as the result of the river bank breaking away at the weir. This must have occurred during the very early 1920's. The miller, early one morning, operated the sluice gate in the usual manner to let water on to the wheel. Nothing happened and there was no sound of water. The water had disappeared from the mill race during the night and all he saw on looking through the mill window was mud![24] For reasons unknown the breach in the river bank was never repaired by Flixton Hall Estate. The mill and mill cottage slowly deteriorated into a ruinous condition culminating in their demolition in 1927.[25]

Mr. Arthur Pearce, who is very much a native of Wortwell, recalls that after the mill ceased working and prior to its demolition, the ground floor was often used for village whist drives, there being no village hall available; this would be around 1924.

It would seem that demolition was carried out without too much care because, even recently, bricks, flint stones, pieces of millstones and gear wheels have been found in the river close to the mill site by Mr. L.P. Hammond who lives in and owns The Mill House and the site of the mill and cottage.

HOMERSFIELD WATERMILL

1. John Munnings, "The Passing of the Country Miller and his Mill, Rivers Stour and Waveney", unpublished article, c.1970.
2. Ibid.
3. Ibid.
4. S.R.O.. (I) HA12/B2/23/1.
5. S.R.O. (I) HA12/C2./70.
6. S.R.O. (I) HA12/C2/80.
7. Excerpts Transactions of the Newcomen Society 1964/1965, p.111.
8. S.R.O. (I) HA12/C2/82.

 9. S.R.O. (I) HA12/B2/17/35.
10. S.R.O. (I) HA12/B1/5/32.
11. S.R.O. (I) HA12/B2/5/17.
12. Sun Fire Insurance Policy No. 366103 (vol. 246).
13. Ipswich Journal, 6th February 1830.
14. White's Directory.
15. S.R.O. (I) HA12/D8/5/1.
16. S.R.O. (I) HA12/B3/9/18.
17. S.R.O. (I) HA12/D8/9/86.
18. White's Directory.
19. Information supplied by Rank Hovis Ltd.
20. Kelly's Directory.
21. Mr. Ernest W.D. Hadingham, Holton, Suffolk.
22. Ibid.
23. Kelly's Directory.
24. R.D. Clover, "A River and It's Mills" Article in Eastern Daily Press, 27th
    October 1954.
25. John Munnings, Op. Cit.

Flixton Watermill, Suffolk

It appears there was a watermill at "Flixtuna" at the time of the Domesday Survey. In the "Domesday Geography of Eastern England", Third Edition, 1971, published by Cambridge University Press, Professor H.C. Darby states:-
"In the same Hundred (Wangford) there was one-fifth of a mill at each of three nearby places — Elmham* (356), Flixton (380) and Linburne (370). Were these portions of one and the same mill? We cannot say. In any case there is the problem of the remaining fractions. On another holding at Flixton there was half a mill (434b) but whether this was part of the half mill at the neighbouring village of Ilketshall (300b) we cannot be sure." He goes on to say:-
"The Group of 6 mills was at Bungay, or rather $5^1/_2$ mills; the missing half may have been entered under Ilketshall or Flixton or yet some other place".

After the Domesday Survey, the next earliest date so far discovered concerning a watermill at Flixton is 1264. In that year an important addition was made to the revenues of the Priory at Flixton by the grant of the rights of a watermill. The publication from which this information was obtained also states; "The site of this watermill, together with some remains of an ancient road probably leading from the Bishop's palace of South Elmham, is associated with a fordable place in the river Waveney, still occasionally used by huntsmen".[1] It is uncertain to which ancient road the author of this statement is alluding. Likewise the "fordable place" is indeterminate.

Another reference to a watermill at Flixton is in a quit claim to an annual rent of 13s. 4d. from a Watermill with appurtenances, Roger de Bosco, son of Peter de Bosco, to the Prioress and Convent of Flixton, from whom the same Peter held the annual rent. The quit claim is dated, Exalt H.C. 28 Edward I, (14 September 1300).[2]

Millers lived in harsh times, from an ecclesiastical point of view, especially during the 14th century. The miller at Flixton in c.1399 was one John Skilley

* This is clearly St. Mary South Elmham otherwise Homersfield and refers to Homersfield Mill.

97

who was "injoined for penance seven yeares imprisonment in the monastry of Langley", and for his wickedness of eating flesh on Fridays, he was put on a bread and water diet on Fridays during his imprisonment. When he had completed his sentence he had to put in four appearances at the Cathedral, with other penitentiaries, two on the ensuing Ash Wednesdays and two on the ensuing Maundy Thursdays. What happened to John's mill during his absence is not recorded but presumably he made some kind of arrangement for it to continue to serve the local community.[3]

A lease of a watermill belonging to the Priory of Flixton with a garden, 3 acres of meadow and ground lying beside the watermill, was granted by Dame Elizabeth Wright, Prioress to Henry Martyn of Earsham, Norfolk, and William Yarham, miller of Wymondham, and dated 10 December 12 Henry VIII (1520).[4]

The manor of Faucons, and lands in Stuston, Broome, etc., were granted to the Priory of Flixtuna or St. Mary Southelmham in the 45th of King Edward III (1372) and a Watermill here (Flixton) was annexed, valued in 1534, at £1 13s. 4d. per annum.[5]

A copy (late 18th century) of a grant of the manor of Flixton which is dated 1 May 36 Henry VIII, (1544), by King Henry VIII to John Tasburgh is interesting. It reads as follows:-

"Do give and grant and by these presents have given & granted to the said John Tasburgh ALL that our Manor of Flixton in our County of Suffolk with all its Rights Members & Appurtenances to the late Priory of Flixton in the same County late belonging or appertaining…And all that our Water Mill of Flixton aforesaid with all its Rights & Appurtenances there and one Garden Three Acres of Meadow & One Parcell of Land with the appurtenances to the said Mill adjoining situate lying and being in Flixton aforesaid to the said late Priory late belonging and appertaining & now or lately in the Tenure or Occupation of William Shelton or his assigns All and Singular Pools Ditches Waters Fisheries Fishings Rivers Rivulets & Water Courses Ways Commodities Liberties Emoluments & Hereditaments Whatsoever in Flixton aforesaid to the said Mill in any Mannor belonging or appertaining or with the same Mill to the aforesaid William Shelton granted or demised."[6]

It should be remembered that by the end of 1539 not only had the smaller religious houses been suppressed by Act of Parliament but the larger houses had also fallen into the hands of the King. John Tasburgh must have been very much in the King's favour!

There was an agreement between Sir John Tasburgh, Knight of Flixton and John Bleverhassett and Robert Cressy that they will bring a recovery against him of the manor of Flixton, Watermill in Flixton, rectory impropriate of Flixton, Southelmham St. Peter, Ilketshall St. Margaret, Bungay and

Shipmeadow, manor of Boyses and messuage called St. Peter's Hall, to the use of Sir John Tasburgh in order that he may establish an estate in fee simple. The agreement is dated 1 October 5 James I (1607).[7]

A note of 1620 exists which refers to a board at Flixton mill which was measured by Benjamin Parkens and Richard Russell for Joseph Brande, the latter being either the owner of the mill or the miller.[8] Quite why the "board" was measured is not known.

A somewhat extraordinary document was discovered in the course of research which again mentions Flixton mill. It is a lease for one year, granted by Richard Tasburgh of Flixton to John Acton of Bramford and dated 1st January 1701/2 of lands in the occupation of — Davy, widow, Matthew Tower, Thomas Chitwick, Daniel Butcher, Susan Hounslow, Robert Brigg and Samuel Robertson in Flixton, of Flixton Mill, of Tithes and woods in Flixton and Homersfield, of messuages and lands in the occupation of Mary Butcher, widow, Richard Jermy and — Baker, widow, in St. Cross and Homersfield and of lands called Hart in St. Margaret Southelmham.[9]

Comparatively recently an article on watermills in the Waveney Valley was published in a local newspaper.[10] The author mentions most of the mills and in particular, it is to be noted, there is reference to Wortwell Mill, Homersfield Mill and Flixton Mill. Regarding the latter he states:- "A watermill long since demolished, also existed at Flixton, near Bungay, and foundations of it can still be seen near the river bank." This is indeed an intriguing statement. Inspite of numerous enquiries, the whereabouts of the "foundations" have not been discovered. Unfortunately the author of this article died some years ago, it was therefore not possible to enquire in that direction. Mr. and Mrs. B.C. Fuller of Oaklands Farm, Flixton Road, Bungay, whose land includes that between the B1062 road and the river Waveney and which therefore has an extensive river frontage in Flixton, have never seen any brickwork or foundations which would indicate the site of a mill. Mr. Fuller has known the land and area all his life and has rowed that considerable stretch of the river over many years. The site of Flixton mill therefore remains somewhat of a mystery. A number of other people who were approached for information on this mill were of the opinion that Flixton mill and Homersfield mill were one and the same mill. The writer is inclined to the view that this is not the case because the Domedsay Survey lists separate mills for Humbresfelda (Homersfield) and Flixtuna (Flixton) and the newspaper article mentioned above is very definite in describing separate watermills for these two villages. Furthermore, John Kirby's map of Suffolk of 1736, although inaccurate, does indicate a watermill at Flixton, the site being at approximately TM 303871. And Emanuel Bowen's map of Suffolk of 1760, to a scale of about 0.38 of an inch to one mile, again shows a watermill at 'Felixton or Flixton'. The accuracy of this latter map also leaves a lot to be desired.

Nevertheless there are two points which are of interest. The first is the fact that the village of Homersfield is otherwise known as St. Mary South Elmham and Flixton is also described as Flixtuna or St. Mary South Elmham. Secondly both Homersfield mill and Flixton mill were at one time owned by the Adair family of Flixton Hall.

During the course of research, plans and schedules of Flixton Hall Estate[11] were examined but no reference or any indication of a watermill's existence was found. Some 20 various documents relating to the Flixton Hall Estate were also investigated.[12] The only reference to a watermill was found in the document mentioned above, namely the copy of the grant by Henry VIII to John Tasburgh of 1544.

Obviously a good deal more research is required to establish the exact situation of Flixton Watermill and also to ascertain when it ceased working and was eventually demolished.

FLIXTON WATERMILL

1. "Records of Flixton, 1915", Richard Clay & Sons, London and Bungay, p.8.*
2. S.R.O. (I) HA12/B2/8/34.
3. The Revd. J.J. Raven, DD, FSA, "History of Suffolk", 1895, p.120.
4. S.R.O. (I) HA12/B2/8/6.
5. Augustine Page, "A Supplement to the Suffolk Traveller", 1844, p.335.
6. S.R.O. (I) HA12/E1/12/62.
7. S.R.O. (I) HA12/B2/7/23.
8. S.R.O. (I) HA12/B1/2/22.
9. S.R.O. (I) HA12/B1/5/81.
10. J.A. Perfitt, article "Watermills of the Valley still thrill", The Journal, Friday 12th November 1965.
11. S.R.O. (I) HA12/D4/23/1.
12. S.R.O. (I) HA12/E1/12/51–70 inclusive.

*There is no mention of the authorship in this publication but A.V. Steward in "A Suffolk Bibliography" gives A.A. Toms as the compiler.

Earsham Watermill, c. 1900. Courtesy of Frank Honeywood.

Charles Marston's 'Garrett' steam wagon outside Earsham Church.
Courtesy of Frank Cannell.

"Mill Holm", Norfolk

NGR TM292866

On both the Ordnance Survey 1 inch map of 1838 and the 6 inch map of 1884, there is a large loop from the River Waveney to the north thereof which forms an island. On each of these maps this is called "Mill Holm". It is about $1^1/_4$ miles west of the village of Flixton and about $^1/_4$ mile south of Low Farm, Denton.

The word Holm or Holme means a river-islet or rich flat land beside a river, from the old Norse word for a small island. So it could therefore be "Mill Islet", which is really indicative of a mill having existed here at sometime.

In the glossary to his book "Old Surrey Water-Mills", 1951 J. Hillier describes Mill-holm as follows:
"A low-lying field near a water-mill, liable to flooding and reckoned to be of more than usual fertility"(sic).

This does not appear to be the site of Flixton Mill but is in all probability the position of another early mill that vanished from the scene ages ago.

Earsham Watermill, Norfolk

NGR TM326887

The site of this mill stands beside earthworks of Saxon or Danish origin. "There has been a mill by the church since Saxon days." This statement is, in all probability, true. Being a very ancient site, it is very likely that a mill really did exist here long before the Norman Conquest of 1066.[1] In 1066 the mill is believed to have been held by Roger Bigod under William the Conqueror.[2] There is little doubt that it was a Domesday site. Indeed the Manor of Earsham was the chief manor of the Hundred, and belonged to Stigand the Archbishop at the Confessor's survey, when there were 3 caracutes in demesne, 2 milles, etc.[3]

Roger Bigod, lord of the manor, also owned the mill in 1086. A later Roger Bigod, who usually resided in his castle at Bungay, was the owner in 1307. It was during the reign of Edward I (1272–1307) that the whole manor was granted to the Norfolk family and it remained in the hands of the Dukes of Norfolk, including the mill, until they sold the latter, towards the end of the nineteenth century.[4]

Earsham Mill is shown on the Suffolk maps of Kirby 1736, Bowen 1760 and Faden 1783, also on A. Bryant's maps of 1824–6.

The lessees or occupiers of Earsham from the years 1651 to 1668 were as follows:-

1651, Thomas Mathewes and his rent was £14 per annum. From 1652 to 1656 inclusive it was John Godsall or Godsalve whose rent in 1652 and 1653 was £25 per annum but for some reason for the remaining years of his occupation it was reduced to £21 or five guineas per quarter. It would appear John Godsalve in 1654 took a lease of the mill for 21 years, but prior to that, from Michaelmas 1651 to mid-summer 1652, i.e., three quarters of a year, no rent was paid because "the same (mill) being till then quite destroyed & in repairing & noo profit made (as the Bayliffe and Mr. Gooch Affirmed) Soe…nil". One wonders what caused the "destruction"; could it have been the result of fire or flooding? Anyhow repairs seem to have been effected and the mill put into working

Charles Marston holding the Jubilee Silver Cup.
Courtesy of Frank Cannell.

order as one quarter's rent of 5 guineas due at Michaelmas 1652, was paid. John Godsalve also leased "the farme of ye mill" at £25 per annum but during the last year of his occupation of the mill, his rent of the farm was £21 for the year.

Thomas Holmes took over the mill in 1657 and he remained in occupation until at least 1668. He paid an annual rent of £21 from 1657 to 1662 inclusive and thereafter £20 per annum. During his tenancy certain repairs were carried out and these were noted in the estate accounts. There was a bill dated the 21st April 1659 for repairing the "floate (sluice) for £3 3s. 6d." In the same year there was an item, "mending the mill wheele" 3s. 0d. and "For nailes to mend the same" 1s. 0d. Again in 1660 repairs to the "Fleete" to the mill and mending the Dams cost a total of £3 19s. 6d. In 1661 a "New Wheele" was fitted which together with "repairs to stables", cost £3 16s. 8d. The last item of repair to the mill noted in the estate accounts was, "part of his (Thomas Holmes) Bill for repairs occasioned by the great Winde 20s 0d." which was in 1662. At that time the people of Norfolk and Suffolk seem to have suffered a similar experience as we did in October 1987 and February 1990.

The accounts for Earsham Manor and Earsham Mill during the above-mentioned period, describe Thomas Holmes as "gent. farmer", whereas "Godsalve" is accorded no such distinction.[5]

In 1793 the mill was occupied by a Mr. Thomas Clarke who was then 24 years old.[6] He was born at Hoxne in 1769 and was the second son of William Clarke of Hoxne Watermill where he learnt the art of milling under his father. William Clarke was also a baker and farmer.[7]

During those early days the mill was a comparatively small affair, two storeys in height with storage space in the roof. It appears to have been timber framed and weather-boarded with a pantile covered roof. Adjoining the mill on the north side was the miller's cottage. There is a somewhat strange story connected with this early mill. It concerns a maiden lady by the name of Sarah Smith who was an aunt of Thomas Clarke's wife. At Sarah's funeral in 1810 she was carried to her grave on the shoulders of four dusty millers and a bolting cloth (used on the cylinder of a Bolter which was a device for dressing flour) was used as a pall.[8]

An advertisement appeared announcing that the lease of "all those Water Mills called Earsham Mills, near Bungay, Suffolk," were to be sold by auction at the Tuns in Bungay on the 9th December 1807, together with the dwellinghouse and buildings belonging. Further particulars could be obtained from Mr. Housman of Lopham Park in Norfolk.[9]

Either the lease of the watermill, house and buildings were sold at this auction or at sometime after because a further auction sale was arranged to take place at the Kings Head Bungay on the 13th May 1836. On this occasion the reversion (in another slightly later advertisement it is stated that the "remainder" of the lease was for sale.[11]) of the lease of The Earsham Water Corn Mill, of which 18 years was unexpired at Michaelmas 1836, "at the low rent of £27 per annum". The advertisement for this sale went on to say the premises comprised the Water Mill and extensive Fishing Rights from which the rent had been paid for 20 successive years; also there was and had been for 40 years an extensive trade. Interested persons had to apply to "Mr. Clark" (sic.) upon the premises, i.e. Mr. Thomas Clarke.[10] This information suggests that Thomas Clarke, in all probability, took a 21-year lease of the mill and premises from Michaelmas 1833. He would then have been about 64 years old.

In 1822 and 1830 Thomas Clarke was still the miller but Richard Narbrough is also given as a miller at Earsham.[12] Both these men were again listed as millers at Earsham in 1836.[13] By 1839 George Pulford and Richard Narbrough are given as millers,[14] also in 1845, [15] and again in 1846.[16] In the year 1850 Richard Copping is cited as a miller at Earsham, also Messrs. Pulford and Chambers.[17] George Pulford and James Thurston appear in 1854.[13]

An announcement, dated December 4th 1855, appeared as follows:-

"To be let by tender for 4 or 6 years from Xmas next. Earsham Water Mill situate within one mile of the Town of Bungay. The mill will be let with the water-wheel, pit wheels, three pairs of stones, Flour mill and all the going gears and machinery as now in the mill, with Dwelling house, stables, Granary and outbuildings; and with 8 acres of excellent Meadow Land including Gardens and yards. Tenders sealed up to be delivered at the office of William Hartcup Esq., Solicitor, Bungay, on or before Thursday 20th. inst. who will give further information. The Proprietor will not be bound to take the highest offer or accept any of the tenders."[18]

Among those who tendered for the mill was Robert Harvey Clarke and he was the successful applicant. He entered into possession of the mill in January 1856.[19]

In considering Robert Harvey Clarke, one gains the clear impression that here we have an astute and enterprising businessman firmly entrenched in the corn grinding trade. After taking over Earsham Mill he soon saw there was a potentiality which could not be fulfilled with the mill in its present state. One would therefore be quite justified in surmising that R.H. Clarke in all probability put forward the suggestion to the Trustees of the Duke of Norfolk that the mill be rebuilt. Maybe the proposition came to fruition through his good offices and persuasive powers.

When it was decided to rebuild the mill, plans were drawn and a specification drafted. The plans were dated September 1862 and the specification which together with the plans, was referred to in the General Conditions of Contract, is dated the 7th day of October 1862. The Contractors, whose signatures appear on the plans and specification, were James Maxim Smith

Earsham Watermill. Rear view of the mill when fully automated in 1975. Courtesy of ECN Ltd.

Earsham Watermill. Mr F E Cannell explains the main switch panel of the fully automated mill to Mr John Mill, 23rd July 1975. Courtesy of ECN Ltd.

and Lewis Bull. In J.G. Harrod & Co.'s Postal & Commercial Directory of 1864, James Smith is stated to be a builder and Lewis Bull a builder and bricklayer, both of Printing House Street, Bungay, Suffolk.

The detailed plans[20] and specification[20] were prepared for the Trustees of his Grace the Duke of Norfolk and were not only for a new watermill but also for a four-bedroomed house joined to the mill by a counting house (office). The plans give no indication as to whom the Architect was although the specification mentions a Mr. Edward Muskett who was the Steward at the time and he had to sign any certificates, giving authorisation to any deemed alterations or differences from the plans and specification. The plans are drawn to scales of $1/_4$ in. to 1 foot, $1\,1/_2$ ins. to 1 foot and details of windows to full size.

The plans are extremely interesting and show a number of features in considerable detail. They indicate the mill itself was 47 feet 3 inches long, 24 feet wide (excluding the rear lean-to section) and 43 feet high to the roof ridge. It had three floors, supported by cast-iron stanchions, and a lucam in the east elevation. Plan details also indicate four pairs of 4ft. under-driven stones and an internal Poncelet waterwheel of 14ft. 6ins. diameter, including the 44 floats or paddles with bracing rods. The pit wheel was 11ft. 6ins. diameter, wallower 3ft. 9ins., and the great spur wheel 10ft. 6ins. The external walls of the main section were 18ins. thick up to first-floor level. Thereafter these walls were $13^1/_2$ ins. thick as also were those of the rear two-storey section. The brickwork was English Bond in red facings and window openings had segmental brick arches. The walls were finished at the eaves and the top of gables with a brick dentil course. The roof was timber framed to a 45° pitch and covered with pantiles laid on reed and plaster.

The floor areas of the mill were:- Ground Floor 1084 sq.ft. including the internal waterwheel and pit wheel areas; First Floor 1133 sq. ft.; Second Floor 1133 sq. ft.; Third Floor 973 sq. ft., giving a total of 4323 sq. ft.

The cottage of two floors was similarly constructed but with nine inch external walls. It had a total floor area of some 1538 sq. ft., and provided an entrance hallway, living room, parlour, kitchen, larder, storeroom, 4 bedrooms and a closet. On the plans the Mill and cottage were shown linked by a counting room which had a front access and an internal door to the Mill. Above the counting room was the "Miller's Bedroom" with access only from the stone or first floor of the Mill.

Although the watermill and the cottage were built to a very high standard, a comparison, between the 1862 plans, an illustration of the mill in 1893 and a photograph taken at the turn of the century, shows a deviation from the original plans, no doubt "executed under the authority of written orders by the Architect and signed by the Steward for the time being of the said Trustees" in accordance with the terms of the General Conditions of Contract for executing Building Works dated 7th October 1862. It can be seen that the Lucam was built some 15 feet to the left, i.e. nearer to the centre of the mill than shown on the plan. The cottage too was not built in line with the mill but stepped back so that it adjoined the mill at its north-west corner. When built in this latter position it was either constructed to form a pair of cottages or, at some later stage, converted to two cottages. Later, the cottage nearest the mill was demolished and rebuilt at the opposite end of the remaining cottage. This somewhat drastic alteration was carried out so that the single storey lean-to extension could be built on to the northern end of the mill. Eventually, the cottages were completely demolished to make way for a warehouse. Neither the counting room nor the miller's bedroom were built as planned.

The General Conditions of Contract dated the seventh day of October 1862, signed by James Maxim Smith and Lewis Bull,[21] is a full and exacting document which completely tied up these builders. It runs into fourteen closely handwritten pages including a "Schedule of Prices of work 'material & labor' for building the Water Mill and Cottage at Earsham". Among the several clauses is one that lays down "All materials, tools, implements, and other matters and things brought on to the site of the Works, or upon lands adjoining, for the purposes of this Contract shall thereupon become, and shall continue to be, the absolute property of the Trustees, and shall be considered as in their possession, the Contractor having only the right of using the same for the purposes of the Contract. But after the Contract shall have been duly completed, the Trustees will return to the Contractor, the tools, implements, and surplus and waste materials then remaining on the ground to be by him removed and cleared away, according to the terms of the Specification". Notwithstanding these terms, the Contractor was also responsible for any loss of tools, etc., whilst in the possession of the Trustees! As one would expect in Victorian times, a clause was included which stated "No work whatever shall be done under this Contract on Sundays".

Another of the clauses stated that "The whole of the Works comprised in the Contract are to be completed on or before the thirty first day of July one thousand eight hundred and sixty three". The work was under forfeiture of the sum of £5 per week for each and every week the work remained unfinished after the expiration of this date. The work could be delayed on authority from the Architect in the case of frost, wet or inclement weather and he would grant an extension of the time for completing the work.

The Schedule of Prices of work makes interesting reading and the details thereof are as follows:-

	£	s	d
Digging per cubic yard			6
Concrete per cubic yard		6	0
Reduced brickwork per rod	9	10	0
Ditto in Heydon Mortar per rod	10	0	0
Red pantiling on reed and mortar			
including 1 x 1 splines & splines)	1	6	0
under bows per square)			
Paving with white brick)			
lumps on edge in mortar per yard)		3	0
Paving with ditto flat in mortar per yard		2	3
Paving with 9 inch pavements			
in mortar per yard		3	1
Lath lay float and set per yard		1	4
Render float and set per yard			8
Colouring with two coats per yard			$1^1/_2$
Fir in scantling per cubic foot		3	0
Oak in do. per cubic foot		4	6
$1^1/_2$ inch iron tongued floor per square	2	0	0
1 inch ditto per square	1	10	0
1 inch straight joined floor per square	1	7	0
$^3/_4$ ledged & braced doors including)			
joints and fastenings per foot super)			8
1 inch ditto ditto per foot super			9
$1^1/_2$ inch ditto ditto per foot super			11
$1^1/_2$ inch plain panelled doors per foot super		1	1
$1^1/_2$ inch plain rebated linings per foot super			$7^1/_2$
Mill windows and frames			
including joints & fastenings per ft. sup.		1	3
Cottage windows & casements including			
joints fastenings & hanging per ft. sup.		1	9
1 inch beaded fascia			5
$1^1/_2$ inch Bargeboards & Capping per ft. sup.			6
1 inch wrt weather boarding per sq.^{r} sup.	1	15	0
1 inch shelving on bearers per ft. sup.			6
Battening walls per sqre		7	6
5 inch iron O.G. iron gutters per ft. run			9
3 inch down pipes per ft. run			8
Milled lead in flashings & Gutter per cwt.	1	7	0
Glazing with 21oz. sht. glass per ft. sup.			6
Glazing with 21oz. picked do. per ft. sup.			9
Painting in oils four coats per yd. sup.			7

At the same time the Builders, Messrs. Smith and Bull entered into a Bond with the Duke of Norfolk's Trustees, dated 7th October 1862, for the performance of Works at Earsham Mill. They were "held and firmly bound to The Right Honourable Edward George Fitzalan Howard commonly called Lord Edward George Fitzalan Howard, The Right Honourable Henry Valantine Lord Stafford, The Right Honourable William Bernard Lord Petre and John Abel Smith Esquire being the present Trustees of His Grace the Duke of Norfolk . . . in the penal sum of Two Thousand pounds". However, if the Builders carried out "the Works in erecting and completely finishing a Water Mill and Cottage thereunto attached at Earsham" . . . "in all respects whatsoever then the above written Bond or Obligation shall be void but otherwise the same shall remain in full force and virtue".[22]

With due enterprise and exercising his business acumen, Robert Harvey Clarke attended at the rebuilding of the mill and installation of the machinery and plant therein making sure all was to his satisfaction.

After the mill was rebuilt, Robert Harvey Clarke took a Lease of the "Corn Water Mill, House, and outbuildings commonly called the Earsham Mill and 7A. 2R. 38P. of Pasture land" for 12 years from Michaelmas 1863 to Michaelmas 1875 at an annual rent of £135 which was payable half yearly on the 6th April and 11th October. The tenant had also to pay Tithe and all outgoings. He had to keep all the machinery described in the schedule "in good repair, and leave them so on quitting;" also "the House, Mill, outbuildings, stables, sheds, bridges, Sluices, Water-lanes, Water-falls, Water-gates in good repair, being found Materials for same; and to clean out and keep free from Weeds, the River, Mill stream, and back ditches..."

The Schedule of Machinery was as follows:-

Cast iron Water Wheel shaft with Neck & Gudgeon, Carriages & brasses. Water Wheel complete. Rack Breast with drawing tackle complete to Water Wheel. Iron Mortice Pit Wheel. Cast iron Cistern to Do. Cast Iron Wallower. Cast Iron Mortice Spur Wheel. Cast Iron Upright Shaft. Bridging Pot and Step brass for Do. Middle Carriage & brasses for Do. 4 Cast Iron Columns & Topplates with bolts, screws, gimps & Keys complete. 3 Cast Iron bridgetrees & bolts to columns. Memel* timber Stonehurst as framed together complete. Cast Iron top length of upright shaft. Pair of Cast Iron Clutches to Do. Cast Iron Mortice Crown Wheel Top carriage brasses & bolts. 2 Flood Gates. Iron Weed rack at back of Mill.[23]

---

* Memel, now called Klaip'eda, is a large city in Lithuania on the Baltic Sea coast. Memel timber is that which was imported from the sea-port of that name and is in effect Russian Pine.

Obviously Robert Harvey Clarke renewed his tenancy at the expiration of his original 12 year term, i.e. in 1875 because he continues as lessee or tenant through to 1892. In trade and commercial directories he is also described as a Corn and Coal Merchant as well as a farmer; and as a miller he used both steam and water power.

At sometime prior to 1893, Earsham Mill was enlarged. When the mill was rebuilt it was 47ft 3ins long. The first extension was built on to its southern end amounting to 30ft 11ins. After a while a further addition was built on to the last one and this amounted to 10ft 10ins. The total frontage of the extended mill was therefore 89ft. Other alterations were made and additions built over the years so that it bore little relation to the original rebuilt mill of 1863. However, the rebuilt mill had eleven pairs of stones driven by water power, with a horizontal engine by Riches & Watts of Norwich as auxiliary power,[24] prior to the roller plant being installed.

In 1877 Robert Harvey Clarke acquired a site on the southern bank of the River Yare at Yarmouth. In the following year he built the Waveney Mills on his site and they were originally equipped with twelve pairs of stones before being converted to rollers in 1886[25] after which the mills had a 10–12 sack capacity.[26]

In December 1882 the Earsham Water Mills were to let. In an advertisement they were described as "a first class flour mill. The machinery comprises excellent Water Wheel and 20 h.p. compound engine, 6 pairs of stones, drying kiln and the best modern machinery". Possession was to be given on the 6th April 1883 and applications had to be made to the Proprietor Mr. R. H. Clarke.[27] The response to this advertisement does not appear to have been recorded but clearly Robert Harvey Clarke continued as tenant from April 1883. It is to be noted that Robert's son Thomas (no relation to Thomas Clarke of 1793) was listed as the miller in 1883,[28] indeed he occupied the mill through to 1897, the year he died.[29] It therefore seems that father and son were working together in the firm, Robert supervising the Yarmouth Roller Mills and Thomas managing Earsham Mill. On 8th August 1893 Robert Harvey Clarke purchased the mill from the Duke of Norfolk of whom he had held it for 36 years.[30] In the following year he obtained details and estimate for a 2-sack Roller Plant from Whitmore and Binyon of Wickham Market, Suffolk. The flow plan for the roller plant is numbered 9094 and dated November 24th 1893 and this firm carried out the installation.

On Sunday 24th March 1895 a severe gale (also described as a hurricane) unroofed Earsham Watermill[31] and at the same time Mr. Clarke's Mill House suffered much damage.[32]

In August 1897, Mr. R. H. Clarke instructed Whitmore and Binyon of Wickham Market, Suffolk to convert the two-sack Roller Plant to a Haggenmaster Plansifter Mill on their latest lines.[33]

On the 30th April 1900, Mr. R. H. Clarke sold the mill, etc., for £1,500 to Charles Marston[34] (1841–1919) who ran it, the Bungay Watermill and the

Harleston Steam Mill until he died on the 14th November 1919. By his Will dated 8th April 1915, Charles Marston appointed his son, Charles Candace Marston and his step-daughter Emily Hancy to be his Executors and, inter alia, devised and bequeathed all his real and personal estate whatsoever and wheresoever including the Earsham Watermill to his son Charles Candace Marston for his own use absolutely.[35] His son Charles Candace Marston (1882–1950) then took over the mills. Robert Harvey Clarke died on the 18th May 1906 and is buried in Earsham Churchyard with his wife, Anne Deborah, who predeceased him by almost eight years.

Robert Harvey Clarke executed a fairly lengthy and detailed Will (undated) in which he granted several annuities and appointed Trustees to administer them. He also executed a Codicil to his Will in which he bequeathed his household furniture and effects and these are listed in detail. Probate of his Will and Codicil was granted to his Executors at Ipswich on the 12th October 1908.[36]

In 1983 BBC Radio Norfolk visited Earsham Village in their series "Village Voice". Among those interviewed was the late Mr. Jack Wilby who was born in the village in January 1901 and lived there all his life — in four different houses. He went to the village school at the age of 3 and left at 13 because he had found a job on a small farm "down the road", at a wage of 3s. 6d. ($17^1/_2$p) per week. He stayed for only four months leaving to take a paper round at W. H. Smith & Son's bookstall on Bungay Railway Station at a wage of 5s. 6d. ($27^1/_2$p) per week. This lasted for two years. His father worked at Earsham Mill and one day he was asked by the "Governor" (Charles Marston) if he knew of "half-a-man" to help in the mill. He said his son was looking for a job (he was then about 15 years old) and he actually was taken on at 9s. 6d. ($47^1/_2$p) per week. Jack Wilby said things were "pretty rough" down at the mill at that time and his job was sweeping floors and so on. At the end of his first week he went into the office during the Saturday morning to collect his wages. The "Governor" sat there with a tray of coins in front of him and handed Jack his 9s. 6d. Whereupon Jack said that it was not half-a-man's wages as the men were getting £1 per week. Charles Marston then retorted "How the hell do you know how much the men get?" And Jack Wilby nearly got the sack! However, next week he was given 10s. 0d. (50p). Eventually things improved insofar as his job was concerned because he was "put on the machines". After 1939, when Hovis took over, he was on shift work "which was much better". Jack Wilby worked at Earsham Mill for a total of 43 years, including World War II.

When one compares the wages mentioned above with those quoted at Ellingham Mill downsteam, it will be seen only a modest increase took place over a period of around twenty years, but of course there was no inflation in those days.

Charles Candace Marston was indeed a well-known miller and successful businessman operating Bungay Watermill and Harleston Steam Mills in

addition to the Earsham Mill. In 1923 he won "The Miller" Silver Challenge
Cup at the Baker's Exhibition for the finest flour in open classes of the British
Wheat Flour Competition. He also exhibited in 1928, 1929, 1930, 1934, 1935
and 1936 winning Gold and Silver Medals, Diplomas and the "Silver Jubilee"
Cup for Biscuit Flour. The company also manufactured their renowned
"Eatwell" Self-Raising Flour and "Eatwell" National Pastry Flour.[37]

Earsham Mill produced both Flour and animal feed and in 1935 the mill was
extended when additional rollers were installed.[38] It then became a 7-sack
plant.

For reasons best known to himself, Charles C. Marston decided to emigrate
in 1939 to South Africa and he was convinced in his own mind that war would
not break out and so he sold the business to Hovis Limited. As war was
declared, he decided not to go to South Africa and he carried on as a non-
Executive Director with Charles Marston (Bungay) Limited, which was a
subsidiary of Hovis. He was in fact invited to join the Board of Hovis, but
declined.[39]

The company of Charles Marston (Bungay) Limited was incorporated on
the 27th July 1939 under the Companies Acts as a private company, limited by
shares with a Nominal Capital of Ten Thousand Pounds divided into Ten
thousand shares of One Pound each all of which were issued and fully paid up
or credited as fully paid up.[40] According to an old Order/Invoice docket the
Directors of Charles Marston (Bungay) Limited, were, C. C. Marston, C. G.
Wood and T. F. C. Holt.

Charles Candace Marston's business was thus absorbed into Hovis Limited
and the two watermills on the River Waveney and a mill in the town of
Harleston were brought into the group. All three had previously been run by
Charles Marston and they then became subsidiaries of Hovis Limited, and
traded as:

> Charles Marston (Bungay) Limited, Earsham, Norfolk.
> Charles Marston (Bungay) Limited, Harleston, Norfolk.
> Charles Marston (Bungay) Limited, Bungay, Suffolk.

The first two were flour mills and the latter a provender mill.[41] Charles
Candace Marston died on the 28th May 1950.

In 1947 Hovis Limited took over Ellingham Mill, further downsteam and in
1949 animal feed production was transferred from Earsham to Ellingham
there being no flour milling at the latter at that time. Flour milling ceased at
Earsham Mill in the autumn of 1962 and animal feed production was then
transferred back to Earsham Mill from Ellingham Mill which was then offered
for sale in 1964.[42]

At an extraordinary general meeting of the Company held on the 1st April
1955, two special resolutions were duly passed. By the first resolution it was
resolved that the Company be wound-up voluntarily and that a Liquidator be

appointed for such purposes. The second resolution authorised the Liquidator to transfer all the assets of the Company to Hovis Limited including "All that messuage or dwellinghouse and Mill known as Earsham Mill with the offices garages outhouses piggery and other buildings, yards gardens and land belonging thereto and the small portion of land and weir adjoining thereto . . . now in the occupation of the Company . . ." Naturally the water rights appertaining to the mill were also transferred and the property was also subject to certain existing rights of way. Mention was also made of a right reserved to Charles Candace Marston by the conveyance dated 31st July 1939 (when the property was transferred by him to the private company), "during his life only to the free and sole use of the eel trap installed at the said mill for the purpose of catching eels". He also reserved the right to enter upon the premises for the purpose of operating and repairing the trap . . . "Provided however that he should not operate such sluice and trap in a manner as materially to interfere with the working of the said mill".[43] Charles Candace Marston was either very fond of eels or he found them to be a lucrative side line and had no wish to relinquish his prerogative.

Earsham Mill was conveyed on the 1st April 1955, from Charles Marston (Bungay) Limited to Hovis Limited. There is a Conveyance of the property dated 13th January 1964 from Hovis Limited to Vitovis Limited, the consideration being £9,708. The mill was then conveyed on the 25th August 1970 from Vitovis Limited to Brooks Vitovis Limited.

In 1956 Hovis Limited amalgamated with McDougall and then in 1961 another amalgamation took place with Rank. Thus the firm of Rank-Hovis-McDougall came into being.

Water power was used at Earsham Mill, with one water wheel up to 1962. The mill also had a turbine producing 35 KVA with a six foot head of water. Prior to World War II, Charles C. Marston installed a 200 h.p. diesel engine made by the Brush Engineering Company of Loughborough. It had four opposed cylinders with a central crankshaft. This engine drove the mill machinery through layshafting and pulleys. It ran comparatively quietly and Charles C. Marston took great pride in showing the engine to visitors by balancing a penny on it whilst it was running. This engine did sterling service during World War II and on one occasion it ran for six weeks without stopping. The mill also had a reserve to the diesel engine in the form of a gas engine of 150 h.p., the gas being produced from coke and water (laughing gas).[44]

When inspecting the gutted and dilapidated mill building in 1989, it was noted in an open-fronted section at the extreme southern end, there were a number of iron hoppers suspended from first floor level. These together with iron stanchions and girders were made and supplied by Spencer & Co., Engineers of Melksham, Wiltshire. Also, at the rear of the mill are two sets of sluice gear by the name of "Radicon" which is a registered Trade Mark and patented by David Brown & Sons Limited, of Huddersfield.

Flour milling continued until 1962. Vitovis Limited started the production of animal stuffs and in 1964 the animal feed business at Ellingham Watermill and Harleston Steam Mill were transferred to Earsham Mill.[45] In 1969 there was a merger with Messrs. Brooks of Mistley and a further merger in 1972 with A. Savill & Co. of Mellis which created the company of Brooks Savill.[46]

The name of Brooks Vitovis Limited was officially changed on the 14th November 1972, to Brooks Savill Limited. Then on the 5th September 1977, this latter name was changed to Brooks Hasler Limited. There was a further change of name on the 4th May 1982 from Brooks Hasler Limited to RHM Agriculture (East) Limited. Savills of Mellis, Suffolk were agricultural merchants who had a mill alongside the railway and they were taken over by Rank Hovis McDougall. Hasler were also agricultural merchants and they had a mill at Ingatestone, Essex and a seed cleaning plant at Dunmow. Their Head Office was at Dunmow in Essex. RHM Limited, was the Holding Company for all the various companies under their umbrella.

The production of the mill in 1971 was around 150 tons of feedstuffs per week, which was achieved with a workforce of 18 men. By 1975 the mill had been remodelled by the installation of new machinery at a cost of more than £250,000. The automated mill was officially opened on Wednesday 23rd July 1975 by J. E. B. Hill, Esq., M.A., a former M.P. for South Norfolk. The result of the transformation, by no less than a technological revolution, was that production of feedstuffs increased dramatically to around 1,000 tons per week with a reduced workforce of 15.[47] The automation scheme provided, inter alia, a new blending plant, additional grinder, pressing plant, warehouse and bulk loading bins and a canteen block. In 1977 a laboratory was added.[48] By pushing a button on the main switch panel raw materials of home-grown cereals, meat and bone, soya bean and sunflower seed were turned into pellets of poultry feed[49] — truly a revolution from the early days of provender milling with stones.

The Blending Bins were built on a site at the southern end of the extended mill building and this site had to be piled to a depth of 9 metres which added some £20,000 to the cost of remodelling. In fact the final cost of remodelling the mill was around £320,000, as opposed to the original idea of £250,000. When the silos were erected, pre-World War II, they were built on a concrete raft and it is said the foundations of the raft comprised four old trawler funnels which came from either Lowestoft or Great Yarmouth. They were sunk into the ground and filled with concrete to form piles.[50]

By 1980 the mill was operated by Brooks Hasler Limited and in November 1981, as a result of "a review of its food production resources in East Anglia", the company decided to close the mill on January 2nd 1982.[51]

The review was forced upon the Company by the loss of an annual contract with a well known East Anglian poultry company who had previously taken 95% of the mill's production.[52] Production therefore ceased, although the mill continued in use as a trading depot for a short while until it was sold in December 1983 to Bri-Nik Foods Limited. The new owners announced plans to turn the disused watermill and 4 acres into a country club and leisure centre at an anticipated cost of £600,000.[53]

Nothing came of this scheme and, in August 1986, Earsham Mill was sold on to Messrs. M. A. Billings and T. J. Harbour whose company, Earsham Properties Limited, now owns the property. The mill building is now in a somewhat dilapidated condition. Various other buildings and areas of the site are used for commercial purposes. These include a coal-merchant's store, coach depot, motor car workshop, and a wholesale and retail agricultural equiment, tool and clothes business. The latter occupies some 75% of the site.

Closure of this, the last working watermill on the River Waveney, and probably in its time the most modernised and up-to-date in the county, brought to an end over 1,000 years of milling on this site. This is perhaps the most remarkable of all the mill sites on the River Waveney or even in East Anglia — indeed, it is unique. It has seen a small primitive watermill of the Saxon era and, over the centuries, larger and more up-to-date mills culminating in an automated modern mill which only ceased operating in early 1982. Milling therefore took place at Earsham continuously over a period in excess of 1,000 years. Truly a singularly exceptional site.

EARSHAM WATERMILL

1. The Hovis Magazine, Christmas 1956, p.26.
2. "Old Earsham Mill", information from Rank Hovis Limited.
3. The Revd. Francis Blomefield, "History of the County of Norfolk", Vol. V 1806, p.315.
4. The Hovis Magazine, Op. Cit.
5. Accounts for the Manor of Earsham, Co. Norfolk demesne lands of Bungay Priory, rectories of St. Margaret and St. Andrews, Co. Suffolk, Earsham Park, Bungay Borough cum Soke, Wangford, Co. Suffolk and Earsham Mills, I Vol. 1652–1668 (RL7), Arundel Castle MSS A 956.
6. "Old Earsham Mill", Op. Cit.
7. "The Miller", 2nd October 1893.
8. Ibid.
9. Norfolk Chronicle, 5th December 1807.
10. Ipswich Journal, 30th April 1836.
11. Norfolk Chronicle, 7th May 1836.
12. Pigot & Co.'s Directory.
13. White's History & Directory.
14. Pigot & Co.'s Directory.
15. White's Directory.

16. Post Office Directory.
17. Hunt & Co.'s Directory.
18. Norfolk Chronicle, 8th December 1855.
19. "The Miller", 2nd October 1893.
20. Arundel Castle MSS 497.
21. Ibid. MSS 474.
22. Ibid. MSS 501.
23. Ibid. MSS 474.
24. "The Miller", 2nd October 1893.
25. Ibid. 1st June 1908.
26. Ibid. 6th September 1897.
27. Ibid. 4th December 1882.
28. Kelly's Directory.
29. "Old Earsham Mill", Op. Cit.
30. Abstract of Title to the Freehold Property at Earsham, 1939. Sprake & Co., Solicitors, Bungay.
31. "The Miller", 1st April 1895.
32. Ipswich Journal, 30th March 1895.
33. "The Miller", 6th September 1897.
34. Earsham Mill Abstract of Title.
35. Ibid.
36. S.R.O. (I) IC/AA2/178/355.
37. Invoice No. 6140 of Charles Marston (Bungay) Limited, dated 5th August 1956, the reverse thereof; and their own 3lb. and 6lb . printed flour bags.
38. Frank E. Cannell of Bungay kindly supplied this information. Mr. Cannell was apprenticed at Earsham Mill from 1942 for 5 years. His Deed of Apprenticeship is dated 10th February 1943. In 1948 he was appointed Assistant to the Manager of this mill. From 1957 Mr. Cannell worked at Haverill Flour Mill after which he returned to Earsham Mill as Production Manager, where some 8,000 tons per year were produced which was later increased to 54,000 tons per year.
39. Ibid.
40. Deed of Conveyance and Assignment dated 1st April 1955 between Charles Marston (Bungay) Limited (the Company), Arthur Warin Collett (the Liquidator) and Hovis Limited.
41. A. H. Dence Esq., J.P., Chairman of Hovis Limited, "The Hovis Jubilee", a brief record of the Company's history between 1898–1948, privately printed 1948, p.p.39, 40.
42. Frank E. Cannell, Op. Cit.
43. Deed of Conveyance and Assignment, Op. Cit.
44. Frank E. Cannell, Op. Cit.

45. Frank E. Cannell, Op. Cit, and Beccles and Bungay Journal 25th July 1975.
46. Beccles and Bungay Journal, 25th July 1975.
47. Eastern Daily Press, 25th April 1981.
48. Ibid.
49. Ibid.
50. Frank E. Cannell, Op. Cit.
51. Eastern Daily Press, 18th November 1981.
52. Frank E. Cannell, Op. Cit.
53. Eastern Daily Press, 15th December 1983.

THE MARSTON FAMILY

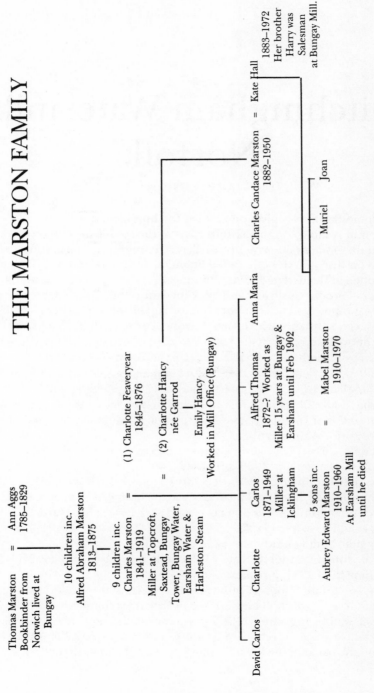

Thomas Marston
Bookbinder from
Norwich lived at
Bungay

= Ann Aggs
1785–1829

10 children inc.
Alfred Abraham Marston
1813–1875

9 children inc.
Charles Marston
1841–1919
Miller at Topcroft,
Saxtead, Bungay
Tower, Bungay Water,
Earsham Water &
Harleston Steam

= (1) Charlotte Feaveryear
1845–1876

(2) Charlotte Hancy
née Garrod

Emily Hancy
Worked in Mill Office (Bungay)

Charlotte

David Carlos

Carlos
1871–1949
Miller at
Icklingham

5 sons inc.
Aubrey Edward Marston
1910–1960
At Earsham Mill
until he died

Alfred Thomas
1872–? Worked as
Miller 15 years at Bungay &
Earsham until Feb 1902

=

Mabel Marston
1910–1970

Anna Maria

Charles Candace Marston
1882–1950

= Kate Hall
1883–1972
Her brother
Harry was
Salesman
at Bungay Mill.

Muriel

Joan

I am indebted to Mrs. Janette Howell, a great-grand daughter of Charles Marston, for the above information.

Ditchingham Watermill, Norfolk

NGR TM334908

The Domesday Survey gives one mill at Ditchingham.

The mill is shown on the Suffolk maps of Kirby 1736 and Bowen 1760.

After the Domesday Survey, the earliest reference to a watermill at Ditchingham so far discovered is one called Fullingmylle at Pirnhow in Ditchingham mentioned in Deeds dated 1399.[1] A fulling mill is one where the weaver's open mesh wool product is shrunk and thickened into cloth. This is achieved by the use of water-powered trip hammers pounding the fabric in water to which was added a clay substance which later became known as "fuller's earth".

The above reference, in the Suffolk Record Office, is under Ditchingham. Pirnhow prior to circa 1541 was not part of the Town of Ditchingham, as it was then called, but detached as there were two manors, one of Pirnhow and one of Dichingham (the "t" was omitted in the earlier spelling).[2] It is therefore somewhat doubtful as to whether this particular mill was in fact situated in the present parish of Ditchingham. This Fullingmylle might instead have been a predecessor of Wainford Mill.

The next early reference to a watermill actually at Ditchingham is to be found in the Parliament Rolls as follows:—
"William de Pirnhow in the 24th. of Henry III released to Roger Earl of Norfolk his right of Fishery from the Mill of Cliffe to the bridge of Bungay, and the Earl granted him a fishery from Bungay bridge to the Earl's Vineyard."[3]

This would have been in the year 1240. The "Cliffe" is explained by a high sandy bank rising behind the meadow grounds.

In a document entitled "State of Bussinifs relating to Bungay Mills" and dated June 20th 1781, it relates:
"Henry Gooch and Thomas Cotton are also owners of the site and foundations where another Water Mill formerly stood Called Ditchingham Mill. This mill was destroyed by fire Anno 1761 and is now rebuilding."[4] However, George Baldry, who lived in the rebuilt Mill House in the 1930's, says, "This Mill House stood on the banks of the River Waveney, and had been burnt down in 1778".[5]

He makes no mention of the Water Mill or whether it was burnt down at the same time as the Mill House but the chances are it would have been. If it was not then the foundations of the old mill must have remained for around twenty years before the mill was rebuilt in 1781. But there is a tantalising and definite statement in a 1975 publication to the effect —

"There was a mill there (Ditchingham) for centuries (the last one was burnt down in 1778)".[6] If this is correct then Ditchingham mill must have been rebuilt after 1761 and again in 1781 (as stated in Auction Sale particulars of 1784). It will be seen that an advertisement of 1778 (quoted below) uses the words, "where-on a water mill stood which was lately burnt down". It is submitted that the word "lately" infers recently rather than twenty or more years ago. If this premise is correct then Ditchingham mill indeed burnt down on two separate occasions.

Whether Henry Gooch and Thomas Cotton rebuilt the mill in 1781 does not appear to have been recorded but it would be fair to presume they did being the owners of the site and the old foundations.

The miller at the time of the fire (1778) was a man named Lock. He was carrying on as a grist miller and quoting from George Baldry's book; "It seem he did not do a very flourishing trade, and his poor old pony was more fit for the knacker than the poke-cart (Miller's cart, so called from "poke", bag or sack). When it was laden with a couple of combe of corn it had a hard job to git along, so when they come to a hill, Lock, who was a very strong man, used to sling a combe out of the cart on to his shoulder, and holding it with one hand push with the other — easy as if it was a sack of straw". He goes on to say that his grandfather "used to tell me he reckoned Lock was the honest'st miller ever born, never taking more'n a peck for every combe of corn he ground, considerin' that his toll. There was others separated the rooks from the jackdaws, that is took out all the fine flour they could with a hand sieve, stealing out of a bushel as much as five peck".[7]

In July 1778 an advertisement appeared as follows:—

"Situation for a Water Mill. — To be sold. — A piece of Meadow-ground containing about two acres and a half where-on a water-mill stood which was lately burnt down, lying at Ditchingham in Norfolk within a quarter of a mile of Bungay. There is a good stream and it is a very desirable situation to erect another mill upon as the river is navigable from thence to Yarmouth. — For particulars apply to:

Messrs. Negus & Bonhote at Bungay."[8]

The site was obviously disposed of and a house and a mill were built in 1781, the latter "on the foundations of a very ancient water-mill".[9]

The millers in occupation of the rebuilt Ditchingham Watermill and house were Henry Gooch and Thomas Cotton. Indeed they seem to have been in a substantial way of business as they were also occupying and operating Bungay watermills, a windmill at Wren's Park, near the Staithe at Bungay and the large Wainford Water Corn Mills. All these premises were held on lease from His Grace the Duke of Norfolk.[10] Unfortunately Henry Gooch and Thomas Cotton ran into financial difficulties early in 1784. An announcement confirming the situation appeared in March 1784 as follows:—

"To be Sold by Auction By William Seaman (Under a Commission of Bankrupt Against Henry Gooch and Thomas Cotton) At the King's Head in Bungay, in the County of Suffolk, on Tuesday the 30th, day of March, 1784, at Eleven o'clock in the forenoon.

I   A Freehold DWELLING-HOUSE and WATER-CORN-MILL, called Ditchingham Mill situate on the river Waveney, about a mile above Bungay Staithe, built in 1781, on the foundations of a very ancient water-mill, with a garden and meadow of about two acres adjoining, late in the occupation of the said Henry Gooch and Thomas Cotton. — The mill hath two pair of French burr stones and is capable of grinding and dressing 100 quarters of corn weekly, the going gears being entirely new, and on a much-improved construction."

At the same time other premises were offered for sale by Auction and these were:—

II   A Blacksmith's Shop and Garden at Ditchingham let to Robert Lovett, blacksmith for a term of which six years were unexpired, at a yearly rent of £5.

III   An Island-Meadow, near Bungay Mills, of about two acres.

IV   The new-erected Water-Corn-Mills on the river Waveney, called Bungay Mills, late in the occupation of the said Henry Gooch and Thomas Cotton. Also the Dwelling-House adjoining the mills, late in the occupation of Mr. John Clarke, deceased. And a Tenement adjoining the mills in the occupation of Matthew Swan, miller, at the yearly rent of £3.

V   A Windmill, and Two Buildings now used as stables, erected on a piece of land called Wren's Park, near the Staithe, in Bungay. The mill was late in the occupation of the said Henry Gooch and Thomas Cotton, and the stables in the occupation of Robert Pulford.

VI   The large and commodious set of new erected Water-Corn-Mills, called Wainford Mills situate in Mettingham and Bungay, upon the river Waveney, near the first pair of locks on the Bungay Navigation, and were late in the occupation of the said Henry Gooch and Thomas Cotton.

Also, an Osier-Ground, containing 1A, 0R, 19P, belonging to the said mills, and a meadow and two small meadows. Also, two Commonages, on Stow-Fen, near Bungay. The above premises are held by lease from His Grace the Duke of Norfolk for a term of which 17 years were unexpired at Michaelmas last, subject to a clear yearly ground-rent of £20.

For further particulars of the above estates apply to James Turner, Esq., and Mr. Thomas Scratton, merchant, in Yarmouth the assignees; or to Messrs. Parnther and Druce, London Street, London; or Mr. John Watson, attorney, in Yarmouth."

The rebuilt Ditchingham mill seems to have been a larger affair than its predecessor. Possibly for that and other reasons it prevented part of the Common pastures bordering upon the Ditchingham Watermill from being greatly improved — quite how such improvement could be implemented is not disclosed. However, when the watermill's occupants were announced as being "under a Commission of Bankrupt" and the premises were to be submitted to Public Auction, the owners and proprietors of commonages and common rights of pasturage, quickly convened a meeting or perhaps more than one, and resolved to appoint Trustees for the purpose of purchasing the mill (but not the mill house) in order to remove the "Hindrances and Obstructions". The persons concerned lost no time in having the necessary Articles of Agreement concluded, agreed and executed on the 29th day of March 1784.

This document recited, inter alia, "whereas somepart of the said Common Pastures bordering upon the Watermill called Ditchingham Mill situated upon the Common River called the River Waveney is capable of great Improvement if the said Water Mill with the Dams Sluices Floats Pools Pens and Obstructions raised or made upon or near the Current Stream of the said River and all Gears Appendages and Appurtenances to the said Mill belonging or appertaining or therewith used (exclusive of the Dwelling House stables sheds and a Piece of Land containing about two Acres part of the said Premises standing lying or being on the North side of the said River or Stream) could be had purchased or bought in for the Benefit of and in trust for the Owners and Proprietors of the said Common Pasture their Heirs and Assigns as Owners and Proprietors as aforesaid and for the better improvement of the said Common Pasture and for removing all Hindrances and Obstructions therefrom And in order thereto it is intended and agreed by and between all and every the Parties to these Presents that such of the said Mill and Premises aforesaid as can conveniently be had or purchased should so be had purchased or bought in by the said Thomas Jenkinson Woodward and William Browne . . ." These two gentlemen were the Trustees appointed.

In the Outney Common Account Book 1770–1821[12] the following appears:—

"Memorandum Respecting Ditchingham Mill.

It has been found by long experience that Ditchingham Mill was very injurious to Bungay Common, by keeping up the Water in the River above its proper Mark. The Mill was advertised to be Sold by Auction, 30th. March 1784 in consequence of which, a General Meeting of the Proprietors of Bungay Common was held previous to the sale at the Kingshead — when it was the unanimous opinion that it would be Right for the Commoners to Buy it —

It was then agreed, that the Mill should be taken down and the Materials sold — That the Cottage & Land should be likewise Sold — and to Remove the possibility of any future inconvenience from a Mill being any more built on that stream the Water Course is Reserv'd as the Right of the Proprietors of the Common."

The same Account Book then discloses how the capital sum necessary for the purchase of the mill was to be arranged —

"To Raise the purchase Money the following plan was adopted —

After Selling the mill gears & Materials as placed)		
on next page the Ball^{ce} of which is)	169 17 1	
* The Cottage and Land were sold to Trustees of		
Town Estate for	150 " "	
Took up by way of Annuity see Miss Smyths		
5 pages forward	100 " "	
Borrow'd of Town Reeve see 4 pages forward	70 " "	
Cash from Fenn Reeves See the General		
Yearly Acc^t. for 1786	10 2 11	
	£500 " "	

* A Pencil note beneath this item reads:

"The Town Reeve upon Payment of this sum to the Fenn Reeves Mortgages this Cottage and Land to Thos. Manning Esqr. for £100 which stands as a charge on this Estate in this Account & the Interest paid Annually — see Town Reeve Acc^t D. G. 1797."

The Commoners purchased the Mill, although exactly what they had to pay for it at the Auction Sale is not specifically mentioned unless of course it was actually £500 as stated above. However, they seem to have lost no time in taking down the mill.

The Bungay Town Reeves Account Book beginning 1776 contains an interesting item concerning Ditchingham Mill. The Account is of Thos.

Manning Esqr. Town Reeve from December 1783 to December 1784. The preamble to the account is as follows:-

"December 7th. 1784. The above Account was then examined, stated and allowed — And the Feoffees request that Thos. Manning Esqr. will continue Town Reeve for the year ensuing — And it is unanimously agreed that the Brickwork at Ditchingham Mill be forthwith pulled up, taken and carried away; Except such part as may endanger the Pinning, or otherwise the House there."

The Outney Common Account Book for the years 1784/86 [13] gives interesting details:

1784	Dr.	Ditchingham Mill					Cr.			
							July to			
July 16	Rec^d. for Mill Gears						Novr. Paid taking down the			
	of T. Cotton as p valuation	}	135	"	"		carpenters work of the			
Novr. 4	Rec^d. for materials at sale						Mill & carrying the			
	by public Auction	}	22	18	"		Materials to place of			
	— of P. Bedingfield Esqr.						sale	6	0	8
	for Grass	}	2	2	"		Pd. for taking down the			
Decr. 3	— by Sale Materials		27	8	"		Brick layers work and			
1785							Repairing the Cottage	10	11	8
Dec^r. "	— " do. do.		31	13	8		Pd. Advertising Sale by Auction		9	"
							Pd. Crying Sales thrice	"	3	"
							Pd. Auctioneer, (Mr. Creed)	1	5	"
							Pd. Excise		12	1
							Pd. Mr. Burke attendance Ec.	"	5	"
							Ablett valuing . . . materials			
							after the Auction		10	6
							Pd. Mefs. Redgrave & Fox			
							Valuing Mill Gears	1	0	6
							Pd. Land Tax 2A/ &			
							Poor Rate 1A/	1	18	"
							Pd. for Removing Materials			
							on acc^t. of a Flood		1	"
							Pd. at Kings head at 2 Meetings			
							of Proprietors on Business	1	17	"
							Pd. Mr. Pennys bill writings	9	8	"
							1786			
							March 1 Mr. Gamble, interest			
							for cash advance & at			
							purchase	15	2	6
							Receipt stamps			8
							Balance carr^d. to Acc^t.			
							See preceding page	169	17	1
			£219	1	8			£219	1	8

Disbursements
1786
March 1   Balance on settling the
            Mill Account Dec. 5th 1786   10   2   11

The item concerning the sale of the Mill Gears also appears in Thos. Manning's Town Reeve Account from December 1784 to December 1785. It states, "Received of Mr. Thos. Cotton for the Mill Gears £135". This confirms that the "T. Cotton" mentioned in the Outney Common Account Book is the Thos. Cotton of the partnership who last operated Ditchingham Watermill. Quite why Thos. Cotton purchased the mill gears is somewhat of a mystery.

An undated "Inventory of Utensils & Materials in Ditchingham Mill"[14] exists in the Suffolk Records Office and it is thought to be c.1800. The exact purpose of the inventory is unknown but undoubtedly it was taken in connection with the purchase of the mill by the Commoners. It will be noted that the item "Mill Gears as finally valued by Mr. Fox £135..-..-" ties up with a detail in the Outney Common Account Book for the years 1784/86 where on July 16, 1784 the amount of £135 was received of T. Cotton "as per valuation". The inventory must therefore have been compiled prior to 1800 and more likely in 1784. It is in fact as follows:-

1 Pair of Brasses Pulleys & Boxes.
23 Mill Bills weighing 54 lbs.
Iron Crow and iron Twigg for drawing the Water Gates.
1 Corn Skreen & Box.
Lanthorn & Wire Sieve.
4 Deals — 3 Hammers.
A Flat bottomed Boat & Tarpaulin covering the same.
A Ladder.

Water Wheel with Iron	30..00..00
Shaft & Gudgeon	10..10..00
Large Cog Wheel	12..12..00
Upright Shaft and its Wheels	30..00..00
Brays and Bridge tree	4..00..00
Two Spur Nutts	4..00..00
Meal through (sic)	1..05..00
2 Pair of French Burr Stones with Irons	54..00..00
Vats & Hoppers etc.	4..00..00
Jogging Screen	1..11..06
Sack Tackling & Ropes	3..00..00
Grindstone & Spindle	11..01..00
3 Water Gates Rovels (?) Rack & Chains	8..00..00
thrustaples & 3 Sills	5..00..00
19 square & 80 feet of Floare at	40..00..00
ten Square of Roof	8..00..00
Tiles on the Roof to the Value of	6..08..00
6 Square of Lining to the Walls	1..10..00
Lean to the Water Wheel	20..00..00
three Ladders	1..04..00
Battens in the Yard to the Value of	5..00..00
The Brick work to be taken down & carried away	40..00..00
at the Buyers Expense leaving the Cottage entore	

Cottage with 2A of Land let at 5£ per Ann-ᵐ	100..00..00
	391..01..06
Mill Gears as finally valued by Mr. Fox	135..00..00
Materials of Mill house as valued above	122..02..00

Ditchingham Watermill, rebuilt in 1781, had an extremely short life, undoubtedly brought about by Messrs. Gooch & Cotton becoming bankrupt. If they had not run into such financial difficulties no doubt the mill would have continued operating with them in occupation and the Commoners would then have had to take some kind of action against them to mitigate the trouble occasioned by the "Hindrances and Obstructions".

Bungay Annual Town Meeting was held on 11th December 1810.
"At this Meeting it is ordered and Determined that Ditchingham Mill House and the Land thereto belonging containing about an Acre and three Quarters shall be sold by Auction at The Kings Head Inn in Bungay and their Heirs and Successors for Ever Shall have the Sole and Exclusive management of the head of water at the said house called the Mill House and of all Ditches Drains Sluices and Floats thereto belonging and also to be subject to a way or Passage from Bungay Common to the Mill House as now used."

In October 1811 a Sale of the Ditchingham Mill Cottage was effected to a Captain Sutton for £325. This cottage had previously been sold to the Trustees of the Town Estate for £150.[15] A document entitled "Release of the Mill House of Ditchingham in the County of Norfolk with a — of a Mortgage term was executed between John Cooper Esqʳ. and Saml. Sutton Esqʳ. & Wife and dated 11th October 1811".[16] This document recites, inter alia, that the cottage land and hereditaments which were purchased and conveyed to the Trustees in trust for the benefit of the township of Bungay but that the Trustees or Feoffees their heirs and successors should be debarred from Building erecting raising or making any Mill Sluice Dam Weir or other such like Work upon the said Premises or any part thereof. Furthermore the Feoffees of the Town of Bungay and their heirs and successors for ever hereafter shall have the sole and exclusive right management and control of the head of Water at the said house called the Mill House and of all Ditches Drains Sluices and Floats whatsoever belonging or appertaining thereto without any impediment interruption or intermeddling.
So ends the saga of Ditchingham Mill.

DITCHINGHAM WATERMILL

1. S.R.O. (1) HA 93/2/3023,3024.
2. Albert E. Fairhead, "The Ditchingham that I knew", The Manor of Pirnhow, Chapter II, p. 9.
3. Lilias Rider Haggard, "Norfolk Notebook", 1964, Chapter IV, p. 62; also The Revd. Francis Blomefield, "The History of Norfolk", 1806, Vol. X, p. 128.
4. S.R.O. (L) Acc. 187/1.
5. George Baldry, "The Rabbit Skin Cap", 1939, p. 21.
6. David R. Butcher, "Waveney Valley", 1975, p. 66.
7. George Baldry, Op. Cit. pp. 21, 22.
8. The Ipswich Journal, July 13th 1778.
9. The Ipswich Journal, March 27th 1784.
10. Ibid.
11. S.R.O. (L) 233/23/4.
12. Ibid.   233/4.
13. Ibid.
14. S.R.O. (I) HA 85/3116/12.
15. S.R.O. (L) 233/4.
16. Ibid. 233/23/6.

Bungay Watermill. D F Pluck.

Wainford Maltings and the site of the watermill, c. 1900.
Courtesy of Frank Honeywood.

Bungay Watermill, Suffolk

NGR TM341898

The Domesday Survey says, "At BONGEIA — $2\frac{1}{2}$ mills".

Another source gives, "At Bunghea Then as now 1 mill; and three (fourth) parts another. In the same (vill) Three fourth part of a mill".[1] This of course adds up to $2\frac{1}{2}$. Yet another writes: "Domesday Mills in Suffolk in 1086 6 mills 1 settlement. The group of 6 mills was at Bungay, or rather $5\frac{1}{2}$ mills; the missing half may have been entered under Ilketshall or Flixton or yet some other place".[2] As one would expect, the area around and including Bungay had its quota of watermills towards the end of the 11th Century.

There is a Bond for the payment of £4. 7s.: Henry Whight, Bungay, Milner, and Edmund Cooke, of the same place, petty chapman to Sir John Tasburgh, dated 18th October 1618;[3] also a Bond to secure payment of the aforementioned sum: Henry Wight (sic) to Sir John Tasburgh dated 28th October 1618;[4] and a Bond to perform Covenants, Francis Flowerdaye, Bungay, miller, to Richard Tasburgh, Flixton in Southelmham, Esq., dated 20th August 1662;[5] all most likely refer to millers at Bungay Watermill.

In the Duke of Norfolk's Estate accounts relating to the "Manor of Bungay Burg: cum Soc.", the rent for Bungay watermill is given as "Nil" for the years 1652, 1653 and 1654.[6] It would therefore appear that either the mill was unoccupied or unworkable during those years.

The watermill which stood at the head of Bungay Staithe, was known as Bardolph's Mill, was part of the manor of Bardolph Ilketshall and extended into the parish of Holy Trinity Bungay.[7] In 1704 John Dalling senior (1665–1733) with Richard Nelson, purchased Bungay Staithe and the Bungay and Beccles Navigation. John Dalling was an apothecary by profession, lived in Earsham Street, Bungay, and was Town Reeve in 1730–1731. He also quite likely owned the manor of Bardolph and most probably the mill as well.[8] In 1718 John Dalling junior (1697–1744) was the owner of both the navigation and the mill as well as the manor of Bardolph. He was also an apothecary and was four times Town Reeve of Bungay between 1729 and 1743.[9] When he died the whole manor passed to his grandson, Sir William Windham Dalling of Earsham Hall, i.e. in 1744.

By 1770 the mill and navigation were owned by the Gooch family[10] but at some time prior to 1775 the proprietor was William Kingsbury. In consequence of a deed of covenant with this latter gentleman , Henry Gooch and Thomas Cotton, merchants and co-partners, became the owners and occupiers of Bungay or Bardolphes Mill. They became first possessed of the mill in June 1775. They completed the purchase of the mill on the 24th March 1778 and became "possessed as Tenants in common by an Agreement with Jas. Dover (who had a Mortgage upon S^d. Mill) and paying him the sum of £1200 and Interest then due thereupon".[11]

In March 1775, the following advertisement appeared:[12]

FLOUR-MILLS
To be SOLD by AUCTION
By THOMAS MILLER

At the THREE TUNS in Bungay, Suffolk, on MON-
DAY the 20th of this inft. March, between the
Hours of TWO and FOUR in the Afternoon, the
following Eftates, if not fooner difpofed of by
private Contract, of which timely notice will be
given in this paper.
LOT 1. THE WATER-MILL, fituate in Bun-
        gay, and the dwelling-houfe adjoining
thereto, with the ftable, bake-houfe, yard and garden
thereto belonging; alfo another houfe adjoining to
the faid mill, confifting of a miller's dwelling, ac-
compting-houfe, and large ftore-chamber.
    The mill was entirely new built, and furnifhed in
a very complete and commodious manner in 1771, is
capable of doing a large quantity of bufinefs, and is
allowed to be the moft eligible fituation in the counties of Norfolk and Suffolk, as it ftands at the head,
and within a few feet of the navigable river to Yarmouth, by which corn may be delivered to the mills,
and flour fent down from thence to Beccles, Yarmouth, Norwich, &c. without any expence of cartage. The dwelling houfe is fafhed, and confifts of
3 low rooms, with good chambers and garrets-over
them, and was, with the other houfe, thoroughly repaired in 1772.

LOT II. A WINDMILL in compleat repair, and
a piece of copyhold land on which it ftands (near to
the faid mill) with a large new erected ftable
thereon.

LOT III. AN OZIER-GROUND, planted about 3
years fince, and now in its prime, containing about
2 acres of land.

LOT IV. Alfo a piece of MEADOW LAND of about
one acre and 3 roods, lying near the mill, held by
leafe for 60 years, from Michaelmas 1774.

N.B. The above eftates are very moderately affeffed
to the land-tax; and the purchafer may have
poffeffion thereof at fuch time as may be
fuitable to him.

Bungay is a pleafant and large market town, fituate
in a fertile country on the river Waveney, running
to Yarmouth, and navigable no further than Bungay,
which caufes great quantities of corn being brought
for fale to the market there, and is only 7 miles from
Harlefton and 9 from Halefworth, both very good
markets for buying wheat.

For particulars enquire at the faid mills, or of
Thomas Miller, who will fhew the premifes.

It seems that the various lots may not have been actually sold at the auction
and perhaps Henry Gooch and Thomas Cotton negotiated their purchase of
the lease of Bungay Mill afterwards. The reason for this suggestion is because
of the fact they did not take possession until June 1775 and did not complete
the purchase until nearly three years later. It is of course possible they may have
been tenants for this latter period as opposed to leaseholders.

One point from the advertisement of March 1775 is particularly interesting.
It states the mill "was entirely new built — in 1771". One wonders why the mill
was rebuilt. It might have been because the previous structure was destroyed
by fire (a not unusual reason) or perhaps because the early mill was small, old
and inadequate.

Nearly four years later, in January 1779, the mill was in fact destroyed by fire.
However, it was rebuilt in the summer of the same year.[13] It was stated that the
"Mills were destroyed by fire and all the stock therein being of the value
together of £3,000 and upwards",[14] a not inconsiderable sum in those days. A
further statement was made relating to the rebuilt mill as follows: "The Water
Lane in which the wheel is placed remaining exactly the same breadth and
length as before the Mills were destroyed and the depth or lower floor thereof

was sunk lower about 6 inches in order the better to admit of a higher Water Wheel than before, which was recommended by the Engineer (Mr. Nickalls) on account that it in consequence of the increased height would work with less water".[15]

During the American War of Independence (1775–1783), Bungay Mill produced flour for export to America, as did Wainford and Ellingham Mills.[16]

Immediately after the mill was rebuilt in the summer of 1779, Henry Gooch and Thomas Cotton occupied it and on the 20th December 1779 they insured "their utensils and stock in their Water Corn Mills adjoining each other at Bungay, brick, timber and tiled, £1,500".[17] It is to be noted that the insurance policy refers to two mills "adjoining each other". This is the only instance of such a description being applied to these premises and it would seem that there may have been one building which was divided into two or perhaps two separate adjoining buildings.

It was in 1779 that Henry Gooch and Thomas Cotton were faced with a difficult problem concerning the inadequate water supply from the river to power their mill. It really amounted to a crisis during an important time of business. It should be explained that from time immemorial the use of water of the River Waveney by the then twelve mills was ascertained and determined by what was termed a Float or bank of brickwork whereby the river is pent up at a distance above every watermill. Whenever there is a greater quantity of water than the mills require then the excess water flows over the Floats. "At a distance of about a furlong and a half above Bungay or Bardolphes Mill and of about a furlong above the Float belonging to the said Mill is a certain Beck called Chain Bridge Beck —". This Beck joins the river on the north side of the town and river at NGR TM337900. It then runs in a northerly direction to a point NGR TM338903 where it turns east, passes under the A144 road and rejoins the Waveney at NGR TM347900. On about the 14th April 1779 certain farmers and occupiers of land, inhabitants of the Parish of Ditchingham, viz. James Cole, Richard Durrant and John Long "employed divers labourers to enlarge, deepen and extend the aforesaid Beck". The labourers continued at work "upwards of three Weeks", resulting in the Beck being made more than two feet deeper in many places and in one particular place it was extended $3\frac{1}{2}$ feet deeper and five feet in width. Upwards of 200 loads of soil were thrown out from the bed of the Beck. After this work had been completed the flow of water in the Beck was increased in depth on an average of from ten to fifteen inches. The increased draught of water within the Beck exhausted the stream between the points of joining it to such a degree that Bungay Mill "became unable to effect half its usual quantity of work within the same time". It was stated that, "The injury to the owners of the said Mill was too apparent and considerable to require particular description here". In order to preserve and maintain the head of water to their mill, Henry Gooch and Thomas Cotton had a "Baulk, or stop of Woodwork" placed across the Beck at its entrance to the river, a few inches above the bottom and four inches beneath the Float or Water-Mark belonging to their mill. After the baulk was placed in position the water of the River Waveney continued to have free passage notwithstanding over the baulk into and through the Beck. Also whenever there was an increase in the height of water by floods or otherwise, the Beck remained open to convey the surplus water off adjoining lands. When the baulk was put in position there was no objection or interruption from the above-mentioned farmers or inhabitants or any other persons. It then remained in its original position for two years until the 16th April 1781 when more than 18 persons held a meeting at the Falcon Inn in Ditchingham and ordered that the baulk should in part be pulled up. A carpenter was then instructed to pull up part to the thickness of about four inches. These persons later threatened to pull up the remainder of the baulk and open the Beck without limitation. Such action would in consequence divert the greater part of the water from the river and "entirely destroy the property of Gooch and Cotton in Bungay or Bardolphes Mill". At the time Gooch and Cotton were engaged for the supply of a large quantity of Wheat Flour for the use of his Majesty's forces in New York and Carolina. As the result of part of the baulk being taken up it was stated they had already suffered considerable loss through want of water being unable to "perform their engagement within the stipulated times". Therefore if the threat to remove the remainder of the baulk was carried out then Gooch and Cotton would be entirely unable to complete their contract due to lack of water to their mill. They would then have been exposed to the payment of damages to their Principals thereby sustaining very great losses.[18]

No document appears to have survived whereby the outcome of this dilemma could be deduced. Perhaps the dissemination of the above-mentioned facts sufficed to deter the removal of the remainder of the baulk. Nevertheless the difficulties encountered after part of the baulk was removed could well have been a contributory factor in their tenure of the mill not lasting for long. By 1784, or possibly earlier, they had run into financial difficulties and were adjudged bankrupt. And so, a sale by auction was arranged by William Seaman (under a Commission of Bankruptcy against these two millers). The sale took place at The Kings Head, Bungay, on Tuesday the 30th March 1784, at "eleven o'clock in the forenoon". The sale comprised six lots and included: Ditchingham Water Corn Mill and House (Lot 1), A Blacksmith's Shop at Ditchingham (Lot 2), An Island Meadow near Bungay Mills (Lot 3), A Windmill on a piece of land called Wren's Park in Bungay (Lot 5), and Wainford Water Corn Mills (Lot 6).

Lot 4 was described as follows:—

"The new-erected Water-Corn-Mills on the River Waveney, called Bungay

Mills, in which are three pair of French Burr Stones, capable of grinding and dressing 130 quarters of corn weekly, late in the occupation of the said Henry Gooch and Thomas Cotton."

"Also, A handsome sashed light Dwelling-house, adjoining to the said mills; consisting of two good parlours, a kitchen, four bed-chambers, and convenient offices, late in the occupation of Mr. John Clarke, deceased, at the yearly rent of £50 10s."

"And, A Tenement, adjoining the said mills, in the occupation of Matthew Swan, miller, at the yearly rent of £3. — The above premises are freehold, and in excellent repair."

(The partners also occupied the Windmill and Wainford Mills). All these premises were held by lease from His Grace the Duke of Norfolk for a term, of which 17 years were unexpired at Michaelmas 1783, subject to a clear yearly ground rent of £20.[19]

William Mann bought the mill in 1784, presumably at the auction sale. He let the mill to an Arminian Royalist by the name of Joseph Hooper who converted it from a flour mill into a paper mill.[20] Joseph Hooper, as a paper maker, insured the mill on the 23rd September 1788, "On his Paper Mill with the Going Gears and Machinery thereto belonging situate as aforesaid Timber and Tiled £1600. On his dwelling-house adjoining not communicating, Brick and Tiled £200",[21] and his name is in a list of paper makers given in Richard Johnson's Address Book of 1793.[22] On the 23rd January 1792, Joseph Hooper, "paper manufacturer of Bungay in the Co. of Suffolk", insured his Water Paper Mill including the machinery therein timber built and tiled situated in Bungay aforesaid £1600,[23] having changed his insurance company.

During Joseph Hooper"s tenancy, writing papers were made at the mill.[24] He died in 1817 and the proprietor or master paper maker in 1816 was given as Susannah Hooper, his wife.[25]

In 1786 a water mill at Bungay was offered for sale by auction and the following advertisement appeared:—

SUFFOLK

TO be SOLD by AUCTION
By Mr. SKINNER and Co.
On Thursday the 15th of June, at Twelve o'clock, at
Garraway's Coffee-Houfe, Change-alley, London, in
TWO lots, by Order of the Affignees,
TWO Capital Sets of FREEHOLD and
LEASEHOLD WATER CORN-MILLS, Staithe-yards
or WHARFS, advantageoufly fituate adjoining and contiguous

to the town of BUNGAY, and immediately connected
with the navigation to YARMOUTH, in the middle
of a plentiful corn country Fourteen miles from NORWICH,
and Twenty-one from YARMOUTH, late the
property of
Mr. THOMAS COTTON.
LOT I. A very defirable fet of Freehold WATER
CORN-MILLS, called BARDOLFES with Three pair
of French ftones, flour and dreffing machines, capable of
completing 100 quarters per week, excellent granaries;
warehoufe, and every fuitable convenience, with a genteel
dwelling houfe and garden; the whole in the moft perfect
repair and order, and fit for immediate ufe.

(LOT II was WARNIFORD Water-Corn-Mill, i.e.
Wainford.)

To be viewed 'till the fale. Printed particulars may be
had on the premifes; at the place of fale, and of Mr. Skinner and Co.
Alderfgate-ftreet, London.

It will be noted that in the above announcement the premises are described
as "Freehold Water Corn-Mills called Bardolphes"; also that it had three pairs
of French Stones which ties up with the advertisement of 1784. It is advertised
as "fit for immediate use", implying that at the time it was unoccupied or
possession could be given immediately.[26] But it will be recalled that the mill
which was bought by William Mann in 1784 was let to Joseph Hooper who
converted it into a Paper Mill. Furthermore Joseph Hooper was still insuring
his "Water Paper Mill" in 1792. One cannot but conclude that there is a distinct
possibility of two watermills having existed at Bungay. The clue may well be in
the insurance policy of 1779 when Henry Gooch and Thomas Cotton insured
"their utensils and stock in their Water Corn Mills adjoining each other at
Bungay, brick, timber and tiled". The operative words here are "adjoining
each other", which does indicate two distinct mills albeit adjoining. Another
clue and very interesting point is that on the 10th March 1786, Joseph Stonard
and Richard Ryland of "No. 5 on Great Tower Hill, Corn Factors", insured
"their House and Water Corn Mill under one roof situated at Wangford
(Wainford) in Suffolk, in tenure of ...., Miller, stud and timber and tiled
£1000". Also their "House and Water Corn Mill adjoining at Bungay in said Co.
in Tenure of George Enington jnr. Brick Stud Timber and Tiled £1500".[27] So
it appears that one of the mills was a flour mill and the other a paper mill. The
name of the person running the flour mill at that time is uncertain but perhaps

Joseph Hooper operated both or it may have been George Enington jnr. A few years later, as mentioned in a subsequent paragraph, a David Walker was the miller at the Staithe and John Lenny Pratt was a paper manufacturer, also at the Staithe. The implication is again there were two mills at Bungay Staithe.

A certain Mr. Thomas Bassett appears to have occupied and run this water corn mill prior to 1788, according to the next announcement of sale.

Bardolfes Corn Mill was again offered for sale by auction "on Monday the 21st July 1788 at Three o'clock in the Afternoon at the Three Tuns Inn, Bungay, in one Lot by Mr. Robert Gayford". The property comprised "a Complete Set of Water Corn-Mills, called Bardolfes, with two Pair of French Stones, and other Appurtenances; together with a Smock Windmill with a capital pair of French Stones compleat; capable of grinding and dreffing upwards of 100 Quarters per week". There were also granaries, warehouses, stable and outbuildings and "a commodious Dwelling-houfe adjoining to the Water-Mills, . . . alfo another small Dwelling-Houfe adjoining at the North End of the Mills". It was described as "all now in Hand, but late in the Occupation of Mr. Thomas Baffett, and his Under-Tenants, at the Yearly Rent of £90". The situation of the mills was said to be "truly advantageous for the Mealing and Corn Bufiness; the Mills and Appurtenances, erected on a judicious Plan". They were stated to be in good repair and order and fit for immediate use. All the premises were Freehold and all were assessed to Land Tax at "only £16 a year, to the Poor Rates £60", and were also subject to a Free Rent of 7s. 6d. The purchaser had to take "the loofe Implements and other Articles belonging to the Mills, at a fair Valuation and to pay for them at the completion of the contract". He also had to take certain fixtures on the premises belonging to Mr. Bassett on similar terms or otherwise agree for the purchase of them with Mr. Bassett or his Trustees.[28]

In this announcement it will be noted the watermill was stated to have "two Pair of   French Stones" as compared to three pairs when the mill was offered for sale in March 1784 and June 1786. It would be interesting to know why one pair of stones was removed from the watermill. Also of interest is the fact that two houses adjoined the watermills.

Once again, in 1790, Chain Bridge Beck features in the annals of Bungay Mill, this time during the ownership of William Mann and the occupation of his tenant Joseph Hooper. Problems of a similar nature as those experienced by Gooch and Cotton in 1779 were brought about by certain persons removing the "Stanch or Stop" at the entrance to the Beck. Joseph Hooper wrote to his landlord requesting immediate action to remedy the problem. His letter was as follows:—

Bungay 20 July 1790

Mr.William Mann

Dear Sir

You most probably have heard that the People of Ditchingham have destroyed the Chain Behind the Blacksmith's Shop and thereby rendered the Mill entirely useless. They pretend that I had kept the Water too high & overflowed their Land, but the truth is, that I really wanted water at the time they complained, nor had the Head been above the Common Level for some time, they had been cutting the weeds & ignorantly began above, by which means the water flowed with greater rapidity than the River choaked with weeds below would admit to carry off & consequently made its passage over their Lands, at which very time I was obliged to shut down for a head. I hope you have got the Papers relating to the Chain from Mr.Stonard, as something must be done immediately. The chain belonged half to the mill, but they have destroyed and carried off the materials of the whole.

I wish to see the Papers you may have obtained from Mr.Stonard to make myself Master of all the Circumstances as soon as possible. —

I am dr Sir Y^r. mo obliged
& hule Sevt

Jos Hooper.[29]

Sometime later, (it is difficult to understand why there was a 17 month delay), William Mann issued a Notice to the alleged offenders, requesting "satisfaction" for damage and injury sustained and the reinstatement of the Stanch or Stop. The details of this Notice are of interest. It was as follows:—

Whereas you, or one of you, with Divers other Persons, did sometime in the year 1790, pullup, take down, destroy, or carry away, certain Stanch or Stop erected and then being across the Entrance of a certain Dyke or Beck, called Chain Bridge Beck, in the Parish of Ditchingham, placed as a Water Stop or Mark, and to prevent the diversion of the Water from the Common River there, for the use of a certain ancient Water Mill, in the Parish of Bungay commonly called Bungay Mill, then and now belonging to Mr.William Mann, and then and now occupied by Mr.Joseph Hooper, whereby the Water was and has been ever Since, and still is, diverted and Suffered to run away from the use of the said Mill, by or through the said Dyke or Beck, considerably below the ancient Water Mark, and the said Mill is thereby deprived of her ancient and accustomed Water, and rendered useless to the great Loss and Injury as well of the said Joseph Hooper, the Tenant and Occupier thereof as of the said

William Mann, the Owner and Proprietor thereof — Now we the said Joseph Hooper and William Mann, Do hereby give you notice, that unless reasonable Satisfaction is immediately made to us, for the Damage and injury already sustained, and which satisfaction we do hereby Demand, and unless also the said Stanch, or Stop, be forthwith put down again, reinstated, or replaced, as it was before, or by some other means, the Water in the said River be preserved, to the usual and ancient Water Mark, for the use and benefit of the said Mill, and the diversion thereof be prevented, Actions will be immediately Commenced against you, by us or one of us, for the same. Dated the Seventeenth day of December one thousand seven hundred and Ninety one.

Wm. Mann

Witness

To John Dale Carpenter   at Bungay
To John   Carpenter at Do.
To W Prentice Shop Keeper Do.
To W   Plowman   Do.
To W Samuel Spence   Do.[30]

Unfortunately the outcome of this saga is unknown but reinstatement of the Stanch or Stop must have taken place because the mill continued in production for some years, and, as has been mentioned, writing papers were made at Bungay Mill in 1793. Whether or not "satisfaction" for damage or injury was made has to remain unknown.

In the Parishes of Bungay Holy Trinity and Bungay St. Mary we find various tradesmen and professional persons listed by name who were considered as "Persons Proper to have Parish Apprentices," or as "Persons liable to take Parish Apprentices."[31] Pauper children were apprenticed out by Justices or Overseers and an apprenticeship was for a period of seven years with the usual written and signed Indenture.

From the lists that have survived for these two Parishes, the following names have been extracted as being of interest:

Persons Proper to have Parish Apprentices or liable to take them:—

Bungay Holy Trinity
1787 Mr. Matthias Kerrison
1793 & 1795 Joseph Hooper, papermaker

Bungay St. Mary
1787 & 1788 Lincoln Matchett, merchant
[In the latter year his name was crossed out].

Persons who have had Parish Apprentices —

> Bungay Holy Trinity
> 1786, 1787, 1788 & 1789 James Fisher, miller
> 1788 Thomas Bassett, miller
> 1789, 1796 & 1800 Matthias Kerrison
> 1800 Wm. Button.

It is likely that of the above-mentioned millers, James Fisher was probably a Windmiller as his name does not feature in any of the many documents or MSS examined in connection with the Water Mills of the River Waveney.

When William Mann bought the mill in 1784, a well-known personality of his day, Matthias Kerrison (1742—1827), purchased the Bungay and Beccles Navigation in the same year.[32] The following extracts from the Diaries of J. B. Scott of Bungay, appertaining to this latter gentleman are interesting:—

"April 12. — Extracting from Ashby's M.S. on Suffolk and Bungay History.

Matthias Kerrison dies this morning at 4 o'clock. He had been ill for seven weeks and had eaten no solid food for 25 days.

In the Gentleman's Magazine for 1827 is the following announcement: "Suffolk, April 12. At Bungay, Matthias Kerrison, Esq., father of Major-General Sir Edward Kerrison, of Brooke, Norfolk, by Mary, dau. of John Osborn of Kirstead, in the same county. Born in an inferior station in life, and enjoying few of the advantages of education, Mr. Kerrison had accumulated, by trade and good management, property of little less value than a million sterling, which is much of it invested in the fine estates of Lord Maynard and the Marq. Cornwallis. His own habits of life were of a very plain kind. He married in 1772 Mary, dau. of John Barnes, of Barsham, Suffolk, and by that lady, who died in 1815, had other children besides Sir Edward."

"April 18. — Mr. Kerrison's remains are being borne to their last earthly home whilst I write. He caught a severe cold in the early part of February and having often recovered from indisposition without medical aid, he trusted in the powers of nature, which were on this occasion unequal to the task of restoration. He was 86 years of age. I am told that Denny of Berg Apton has taken the Bungay Staithe and premises. (The Staithe House, in which he lived for so many years has been pulled down).'[33]

With diligence and thoughtfulness Joseph Hooper executed his Will in 1811. It was drawn as follows:—
"This is the last Will and Testament of me Joseph Hooper of Bungay in the County of Suffolk papermaker First I desire that all my just debts and funeral

expenses and other Charges indent thereto shall be fully paid and satisfied and from and after the payment thereof I do hereby Give and Bequeath to my beloved Daughters Emily Hooper and Harriet Hooper respectively and to each of them fifty pounds to be paid by my Executrix herein after named as soon as conveniently can be next after my Decease and I do hereby Give and Bequeath all the rest residue and Remainder of my personal Estate and Effects of what nature or kind soever or whereforever the same be or do consist whith I shall be possessed of Interested in or Intitled unto at the time of my Decease unto my Dear and Loving Susannah Hooper late called Susannah Taylor of Grantham in the County of Lincoln Spinster to and for her use benefit and Disposal for ever and I do hereby Nominate Constitute and appoint the said Susannah my Wife Sole Executrix of this my last Will and Testament Hereby Revokeing all and every Will and Wills by me at any time heretofore made Do Declare this contained in one Sheet of paper to be my last Will and Testament In Witness whereof I the said Joseph Hooper have unto set my hand and Seal this twenty Eighth day of June in the Year of our Lord One Thousand Eight Hundred and Eleven
Signed Sealed published and Declared
by the said Joseph Hooper as and for his last
Will and Testament In the presence of us who   Joseph Hooper
in his presence and in the presence of each
other have Subscribed our Names as Witnesses
hereto
          John Day
          Jnº Holmes" [34]

Prior to 1829 James Betts seems to have been at the mill but in 1829 an announcement appeared to the effect that "James Betts formerly of Bungay, Suffolk, Paper Maker, and late of Upper and Lower Sheringham, both in Norfolk in partnership with Lewis Betts, as Paper Maker and Stationer, Bankrupt".[35]

Then the following advertisement appeared:—

"To be sold by auction on 25 January 1830, at the Kings Head Inn, Bungay. All those freehold premises consisting of a Water Mill, with a dwelling house attached, situate and standing near the Staithe, In Bungay, and lately occupied, in the manufactury of paper, by William Betts.
The Mill is fitted up with every convenience for the manufacturing of paper." [36]

An advertisement announcing the same sale appeared in a local newspaper as follows:—
"To be sold on Jan. 25 at Bungay. All those valuable freehold premises Consisting of a Watermill, with a Commodious dwelling-house and garden

attached, situate and standing near the Staithe in Bungay, in the county of Suffolk, and lately occupied in the manufacture of paper by William Betts.

The mill consists of an extensive range of well built and substantial buildings, fitted up with every convenience for the carrying on the manufacturing of paper, in addition to which the various powerful wet and dry presses, bleaching and other apparatus will be sold therewith.

The premises are altogether calculated for, and capable of carrying on a most extensive trade, and such is its situation that the demand has hitherto, at all times, kept pace with supply. Possession at Lady Day." [37]

James, Lewis and William Betts would appear to have all been connected in the making of paper but in exactly what capacity or how they were related to one another is not known.

It is not known who bought the mill in 1830 but an Excise General Letter dated 8th December 1830 gives a change of occupation at Mill No. 255 at Bungay in the Norwich Collection, the occupier now being one John Creaset.

The mill is shown on Bryant's maps of 1824/26; also on the Ordnance Survey 6 inch map of 1838 as a "Paper Mill".

It should be explained that paper, like many other commodities, was subject to Excise Duty. In 1816 the Excise Office in London prepared a numerical list of paper mills and board mills or factories which gave the names of the mills in question together with the names of the makers. Each mill was given an Excise Number for the purpose of identification. Mills subject to the Excise Duty were grouped for the collection of the duty. These groups were known as "Collections". [38] Bungay Paper Mill was in the Norwich Collection and in the Excise General Letter of the 8th October 1816, when mills were allocated the Excise Numbers, Susannah Hooper was given the number 255 for her paper mill at Bungay. However, in a check list issued on the 28th November 1832, the Excise No. 255 was stated to be not in use. Then in an Excise General Letter dated the 1st July 1833, a change of occupation at Paper Mill No. 255 was notified at Bungay in the Bungay Division of the Norwich Collection to one John Burgess. In 1844 Charles Burgess was listed as a paper maker at the Staithe, Bungay. [39]

In 1850 David Walker is shown as a "miller" at the Staithe [40] but in a Return to the Excise Office, Bungay Mill had one beating engine which was in use in 1851. (A beating engine was a machine for the macerating of rags and other materials into a pulp for paper making). Then in 1858 John Lenny Pratt was given as a paper manufacturer at the Staithe. [41]

One can only conclude that either David Walker was erroneously listed as a miller because a mill had not then been reconverted to a flour mill, or there may have been two mills as previously suggested.

In 1864 the mill "was again burned to the ground, rebuilt and used as a flour mill".[42] At the time of the mill's destruction Benjamin Ward was the occupier and he too was a paper manufacturer.[43] The mill site was then bought by Charles Marston who actually rebuilt the mill in the early 1870's.[44] In fact he is listed in 1874 as being a corn miller at "New Mill", Staithe Road, Bungay.[45] Charles Marston continued at Bungay mill until he died in 1919, thereafter his son, Charles Candace Marston, took over. In 1879, Charles Marston is listed as a "Miller, corn merchant and carter" at Bungay Watermill,[46] and in 1883 he is additionally described as an "hop merchant".[47]

In trading at Bungay Staithe, Charles Marston's enterprise was following a long line of trading concerns facilitated by the opening up of navigation on the Waveney in 1670. On October the 24th of that year by Act of Parliament, navigation was extended to the town of Bungay by the construction of locks at Geldeston, Shipmeadow, Ellingham and Wainford. Owners of Bungay Staithe and navigation are listed from 1673 through to 1919 and one, Matthias Kerrison made a fortune by an extensive trade in timber, coals and corn during the French war. He was the owner from 1783 until he died in 1821 when all his property in Bungay was sold by his son, Sir Edward Kerrison. Matthias's estate amounted to almost £1,000,000 sterling a vast sum in the early part of the 19th century.[48]

The mill appears on the Ordnance Survey 6 inch map of 1884 as a "Corn Mill". During that year Charles Marston was considering an alternative or supplementary means of powering his Bungay watermill, eventually deciding to effect an important intention. In September of 1884 he placed an advertisement in an appropriate publication, which read as follows:-

"Wanted to purchase, in good preservation, a 5 or 6 horse power steam engine, with 7 or 8 h.p. boiler; what maker and when last at work. Charles Marston, Water Mill, Bungay, Suffolk."[49]

He must have acquired a steam engine to his requirements because by 1892 he was listed as a miller at Bungay using both water and steam power. Indeed his mill is also described then as a "Roller Mill".[50]

Charles Marston was again advertising for more equipment in 1890, this time for a water wheel — "Wanted an undershot Water Wheel 12ft. to 15ft. high, 10ft. to 16ft. wide, with first motion wheels. Secondhand or new. Apply to Charles Marston, Water Mill, Bungay".[51]

Prior to this advertisement, Charles Marston had turned his mind to further improving and modernising his Bungay watermill. He requested an estimate from Messrs. E.R. & F. Turner of 82 Mark Lane, London EC., who also had works at St. Peter's & Grey Friars, Ipswich, Suffolk.

They submitted a detailed estimate to Mr. Charles Marston at the Water Mill, Bungay, dated 2nd August 1889. The estimate was for an "Intermittant Plant to produce from half to one sack of flour per hour". It amounted to £408 14s. 6d., less 10% discount of £40 17s. 5d. = £367 17s 1.d., plus £100 for labour to erect the plant. The total cost therefore was £467 17s. 1d. but it did "not include the connection from motion to shaft".

The letter attached to the estimate and addressed to Mr. C. Marston, Bungay is as follows:-

"Dear Sir,

Herewith we send you plan and estimate for a roller plant on the intermittant system and which can be driven by an 8 horse power water wheel. It would produce about $^1/_2$ to $^3/_4$ of sack per hour of flour. We would send a competent miller to start this plant and work it for a fortnight. We may mention that we supplied just such a plant for a mill in France and that the miller was delighted with it. Our price includes everything except the bins which could be made by a local carpenter under the directions of our foreman.

Hoping to be favoured with your order.

Yours faithfully,

E.R. & F. Turner." [52]

It is not recorded whether this estimate was actually accepted. In any event it is usual for more than one estimate to be obtained and Charles Marston may have received one from that other well-known firm of mill engineers, Whitmore & Binyon of 64 Mark Lane EC and Wickham Market, Suffolk. However the fact that the letter and estimate from E.R. & F. Turner were retained by Charles Marston may well indicate that this firm carried out the installation in late 1889 or during 1890.

Charles Marston was a very particular man and he maintained Bungay Mill in good condition. The corrugated iron sheeting to the roof and on the extended hoist was painted in red ochre every five years. No grass or weeds were allowed to grow around the mill. Unfortunately Charles Marston had to have a leg amputated due to gangrene having set in. The operation was carried out on his kitchen table and the leg was buried under one of the apple trees in the garden of the mill house, adjacent to the Water Mill! [53]

There is a rather amusing story relating to one of Mr. Marston's employees at Bungay Mill. This was a Mr. Billy Patrick, a carter, who was affectionately known as "Midnight". He drove a two-horse covered wagon delivering corn and flour to customers in the villages known as "The Saints" i.e. the South Elmhams and Ilketshalls. He loaded up in the mornings, leaving the mill around 11 a.m., but he had a habit of calling at a number of public houses. As a result he arrived home around 10 p.m. to midnight, usually the latter and hence his nickname. One evening Billy felt rather thirsty and decided to patronise his local pub. On his way he passed beneath a large oak tree when he suddenly stopped as he heard a voice from God telling him to give up the drink. This he did and promptly joined the Salvation Army in Bungay of which he was a staunch member until it was disbanded after which he regularly attended St. Mary's Church.[54]

Fire struck again at Bungay Mill on February 25th 1902 and the building was very badly damaged. Some sixty years after the event, details of the fire were recalled by Mr. Albert E. Patrick, who was a schoolboy at the time of the disaster. An account was printed in a local newspaper in response to a correspondent's enquiry. The alarm was given about 2.15 a.m. and the two horses, which pulled the covered wagon his father (Billy or Midnight) used, perished in the fire.[55] The mill was repaired and worked again for many years.

In an old photograph of Bungay Mill taken immediately after the fire of February 1902, a tall brick chimney shaft is clearly shown still standing. This indicates that the mill was also driven by a steam engine. However, in November 1910, Charles Marston advertised an "Iron Water Wheel for sale, with or without gear. Apply to C. Marston, Bungay".[56] It would appear that he had decided to remove the old water wheel from his mill at Bungay but whether it was actually taken out seems doubtful because in the mid-1930's he is described in a Trades Directory as using water and steam at this mill.

Charles C. Marston, the son of the previous Charles Marston was described as the miller in 1920–21 at Bungay & Earsham Roller Mills.[57] Also again in 1933 and 1937 he was the miller (Flour and Grist), self-raising flour manufacturer, corn and coal merchant etc., Earsham Mill (water and steam) also at Bungay (water and steam) and Harleston (gas and oil), Railway Station.[58]

Mr. Harry Hall, aged 98 of Dickleburgh relates that after the Great War, in which he served in the R.A.M.C., and was wounded in the Somme battle, he took over the self-raising flour plant which was run in conjunction with Bungay Mill. The plant was not actually in the mill but was situated about 100 yards away from it in the premises now occupied by the Staithe Garage. Mr. Hall sold the self-raising flour and the ordinary flour over a wide area to customers from Ipswich to King's Lynn, Norwich, etc. The flour was generally sold in 10 stone bags and on one occasion he had 8 tons delivered to one firm in a week. Mr. Hall was brother-in-law to Charles Candace Marston, the latter having married Kate Hall (1883–1972), Mr. Hall's sister.

At sometime after the mill was rebuilt, a turbine was fitted by Gilbert, Gilks & Gordon of Kendal. It was installed on an Agreement that if the turbine would not do the work of the waterwheel (which was to be removed), then the waterwheel was to be replaced and the turbine taken out. Eventually the turbine was removed and the waterwheel put back![59]

By 1948 Hovis Limited had taken over Bungay Mill and it is listed by them as a Provender Mill and was one of their subsidiary companies known as Charles Marston (Bungay) Limited, Bungay, Suffolk.[60] (See under Earsham Mill). When the mill was last rebuilt, the main section was constructed of brick under a roof clad with corrugated iron sheets. The window frames are cast iron and there are iron stanchions inside supporting the various timber floors. The extended hoist (over the roadway) to the Staithe is timber-framed and also clad in corrugated iron sheeting. There is a three storey section attached, also a lean-to single storey section. On the opposite side of the mill yard is a single-storey brick built building which is part of the curtilage of the mill property and contains at the river end, the mill office. Wherries used to come up the Staithe and load up from the extended hoist.

A Mr. Green purchased the mill in 1955/56 and he says at that time it was still producing flour and the then owner was also selling coal, but the mill was more likely producing feed stuff. The machinery and waterwheel were removed after the mill was sold and the buildings were used for a boat builders and designers business. Prior to the mill being sold in 1955/56 the mill stream came up to the brick wall of the mill and adjoined the footpath running north from the mill. (See O.S. Sheet 1927 Norfolk XCVIII.II Suffolk VIII.II). A large part of the stream has recently been filled in and grassed over such that the bank is now further out into the stream. There was a brick wall at the west end of the mill yard, now demolished, but the footings can still be seen.

BUNGAY WATERMILL

1. "Victoria County History, Suffolk " Vol. I, p.441.
2. Prof. H.C. Darby, "The Domesday Geography of Eastern England", Third Edition, 1971, p.190.
3. S.R.O. (I) HA12/B1/2/15.
4. S.R.O. (I) HA12/B1/2/16.
5. S.R.O. (I) HA12/B2/19/24.
6. Arundel Castle Archives, MSS A956.
7. Ethel Mann, "Old Bungay", 1934, p.148.
8. John Harris "The Town Reeves of Bungay 1725–1896, A Study of a Unique and Ancient office and those who have occupied it", 1986.
9. John Harris, Ibid.
10. Ethel Mann, Op. Cit.
11. S.R.O. (L) Acc. 187/1 MSS "State of Bussinifs relating to Bungay Mills, June 20th 1781".
12. Ipswich Journal 11th March 1775.
13. S.R.O. (L) Acc. 187/1 Op. Cit.
14. S.R.O. (L) Acc. 187/1 Op. Cit.

15. S.R.O. (L) Acc. 187/1 Op. Cit

16. Rank Hovis Limited, undated article, "Mills Past and Present on the River Waveney".

17. Sun Fire Insurance Policy No. 422228 (vol. 278).

18. S.R.O. (L) Acc. 187/1 Op Cit.

19. Ipswich Journal 27 March 1784.

20. Ethel Mann, Op. Cit.

21. Sun Fire Insurance Policy No. 548408 (vol. 356).

22. A.H. Shorter, M.A., Ph.D., "Mills and Paper Makers in England, 1495–1800".

23. Royal Exchange Fire Insurance Policy No. 126221.

24. A.H. Shorter, Op. Cit.

25. Ibid.

26. Ipswich Journal 27 May 1786, p.3.

27. Sun Fire Insurance Policy No. 516092 (vol. 334).

28. S.R.O. (L) Acc. 187/1 MSS & Notes compiled by Ethel Mann, 17th to 19th cent. for her book "Old Bungay".

29. Ibid.

30. Ibid.

31. S.R.O. (L) Acc. 187/2.

32. Ethel Mann, Op. Cit. (amended).

33. "An Englishman at Home and Abroad 1792–1828, Being Extracts from the Diaries of J.B. Scott of Bungay, Suffolk", edited by Ethel Mann, reprinted with additional notes by Peter Morrow, 1988, p.p. 210 and 211.

34. S.R.O. (I) IC/AAI/233/1.

35. London Gazette, June 26, 1829.

36. London Gazette, January 15, 1830.

37. Ipswich Journal, January 9, 1830.

38. A.H. Shorter, M.A., Ph.D., "Paper Making in the British Isles, An Historical and Geographical Study", 1971, p.p. 122 and 123.

39. White's Directory.

40. Hunt & Co.'s East Norfolk Directory.

41. Post Office Directory, Cambs., Norfolk and Suffolk.

42. Ethel Mann, Op. Cit.

43. Harrod & Co.'s Directory.

44. John Munnings, 'The passing of the Country Miller and his Mill, Rivers Stour and Waveney". Unpublished article, c. 1970.

45. White's Directory.

46. Kelly's Directory.

47. Ibid.

48. Ethel Mann, Op. Cit., p.147.

49. "The Miller", September 1, 1884.

50. Kelly's Directory.
51. "The Miller", December 1, 1890.
52. Original letter and estimate kindly loaned by Mr. F.E. Cannell of Bungay.
53. Mr. A.F. Jermy of Bungay kindly supplied this information.
54. Mr. A.F. Jermy, Ibid.
55. "The Journal", January 20, 1961, et. seq.
56. "The Miller", November 14, 1910.
57. Eastern Counties of England Trades Directory 1920–21.
58. Kelly's Directories.
59. John Munnings, Op. Cit.
60. A.H. Dence, Esq., J.P., Chairman of Hovis Limited, "The Hovis Jubilee".
    A Brief record of the Company's history between 1898–1948, privately
    printed, 1948, p.40.

Wainford Watermill, Suffolk

(The larger part of the mill was in Suffolk
with a small part in Norfolk)

NGR TM351902

IN the Domesday Survey there is mention of Pirnhow "Now 1 mill". The manor of Pirnhow was to the east of Bungay and included what is now called Wainford. The earliest information concerning the Lordship of Pirnhow is that Roger Bigod, an ancestor of the Earls of Norfolk, deprived Algar, a freeman, of it when he held it under Stigand the Archbishop of Canterbury around the year 1050. William de Pirnhow held the Lordship under Bigod in the reign of Henry I, 1100 to 1135.[1]

Around 1180 two mills are mentioned in an action before the King's Justices at Westminster between William de Pirnhow and William de Brom concerning a water course in the town of Pirnhow. It was agreed that the two Williams should destroy their two mills and erect one mill on the water course belonging to both and that each should have an equal right in the one new mill. From this it appears that mills existed before 1180 and on the water course where the maltings stood. They were most likely used for grinding and storage of corn.[2]

The mill is again mentioned in 1178. This was in connection with a right of fishery which William de Pirnhow released to Roger, Earl of Norfolk, by fine from the mill to the bridge of Bungay. In return he was granted a fishery right from the same bridge to the Earl's vineyard.[3] Around 1550 the mills were known as Wangford Mills. They are shown on Kirby's map of Suffolk 1736, Faden's maps of Suffolk 1783 and Norfolk 1797, also on A. Bryant's maps of 1824–26 but as "Wangford Mill". The mill is also shown on the First Edition of the Ordnance Survey 1 inch map of 1837 and 6 inch map of 1884.

In 1444 John de Martlesham was stated to be at Wainford Mill and his trade was that of a fuller. Maybe an early mill here was used for fulling.

Quite early references to Wainford Mill appear in old estate accounts of the Duke of Norfolk's manor of Bungay Priory. For example, the rent for

"Wangford Mill" for the years 1652 to 1657 inclusive was £12 per annum but there is no note of the name of the occupier of the mill during these years. Probably the reason for this omission is the fact that the mill was then described (in the accounts), as "Percell of ye Priory". Therefore the estate itself was not particularly interested in the name of the occupier, only in receiving the rent from the Priory. In 1656 William ffrancis was paid 49 shillings "for board and Trundles used about the Mill Gates and Mill Wheels". There is an entry in these accounts for "Wangford Mill" in 1659 for £21 and again in 1660 for £22 but it is not stated what is represented by these amounts. Also in the year 1660 there were repairs to the mill amounting to the sum of £11 14s. 4d., and "taxes" for the mill for the same year were £2 16s. It appears that Samuel ffuller was occupying the mill in 1663 as there is an entry in the accounts "for one yeares rent for Wangford Mill ended att ye Lady day last £4". Samuel ffuller paid £8 rent for the mill in 1664 and in 1665 there is an entry "Arrears upon Sam: ffuller for Wan: Mill £8" but the rent appears to have been paid later.[4] There is no indication as to why his rent was doubled but it may well have put him under strain.

In 1688 a survey was carried out for the Duke of Norfolk of the manors of the Borough of Bungay, Bungay Soke, Bungay Priory and North Hales, all County of Suffolk, taken by Thomas Hornebye and written in Latin. It mentions a meadow with a water mill called "Waynford" Mill being held at the time by Thomas Walcott, gentleman bailiff of the Manor of Bungay. He also owned Bungay Staithe and the Navigation from 1673 until his death in 1701 when they passed into the hands of his Executors who held them until 1704. "Waynford" Mill is again mentioned later in the survey but on this occasion as a reference point.[5]

We now move on ninety years to 1778 when Henry Gooch of Yarmouth and Thomas Cotton of Bungay in Suffolk, millers, insured "their Water Corn Mill and going gears therein called Wangford (sic) Mill Timber and tiled situate in the Parish of Mettingham in Suffolk £1000". This was on the 21st March 1778.[6] On the 4th February 1779 these two millers insured their utensils and stock in the same mill for £1000.[7] Flour produced at Wainford Mills,(also at Bungay and Ellingham Mills), was exported to America in the days of the American War of Independence (1775–1783).[8]

It was in 1784 that Henry Gooch and Thomas Cotton encountered financial difficulty culminating in a Sale by Auction by William Seaman (under a Commission of Bankrupt against them) at the King's Head in Bungay, Suffolk, on Tuesday the 30th day of March 1784. There were six lots of property offered, four of which were in the occupation of Henry Gooch and Thomas Cotton, including Wainford Mills. The latter were described in the auction advertisement as follows:-

"VI. The large and commodious set of new erected WATER-CORN-MILLS, called Wainford Mills, situate in Mettingham and Bungay, upon the river Waveney, near the first pair of locks on the Bungay Navigation.
— These mills have five pair of French burrstones, are capable of grinding and dressing 250 quarters of corn weekly, and were late in the occupation of the said Henry Gooch and Thomas Cotton.
N.B. The parishioners of Mettingham pay by agreement 50s. yearly, towards the repairs of the road leading to the mills."

Also, An OSIER GROUND, a meadow, two small meadows.
Also two COMMONAGES. The above premises were held by lease from the Duke of Norfolk for a term of which 17 years were unexpired at a ground rent of £20.[9]

There is an Insurance Policy dated the 10th March 1786 which relates to Joseph Stonard and Richard Ryland, No. 5 on Great Tower Hill, Corn Factors. They insured their "House and Water Corn Mill under one roof situate at Wangford, Suffolk in tenure of ... Miller, Stud and Timber and tiled £1000".[10] Presumably these gentlemen bought the mill at auction and they also purchased the watermill at Bungay which was offered for sale by auction as Lot 4 in 1784.

Within an extremely short space of time, the personal and/or business circumstances of Messrs. Stonard and Ryland changed dramatically. Only three months after taking out insurance on their mills at Wainford and Bungay, they were advertised as being for sale by auction. A sale was in fact arranged to take place on the 15th June 1786, at Garraway's Coffee House, Change Alley, London, by order of the Assignees. Lot 1 was the Bungay Water Corn Mill, called Bardolfes, and Lot 2 was Wainford Mills which were advised as:-

"The most complete set of WATER CORN-MILLS in the county, called WARNIFORD (sic), with Five pair of French stones, flour and dressing machines, capable of completing 200 quarters per week, excellent granaries, warehouses and miller's dwelling, a Staithe-yard with range of commodious warehouses and every suitable convenience for a general merchant; the whole completed within six years at an immense expense; also, several pieces of land. The whole held of the Duke of Norfolk, at a ground rent of only £20 per annum."[11]

It is therefore indicated that Wainford Mill, Miller's House and the other buildings were erected c. 1780.

The result of this Auction sale is not known but on the 22nd October 1788, William Mann of Syleham in Norfolk (sic), Miller, insured the "Wainford Water Corn Mills adjoining situate on the River Waveney in the Parishes of Bungay and Mettingham in Suffolk, Brick, stud, timber and tiled £500.

Utensils and stock £500".[12]

William Mann was what might be termed a substantial business man, owning no less than four of the watermills on the River Waveney, i.e. Syleham, Weybread, Wainford and Bungay.

William Mann's ownership continued for a considerable time for in 1839 he and Richard Mann are listed as millers at Wainford Mill.[13] However, although in 1844 they are listed as maltsters, corn and flour merchants at Wainford,[14] Richard is shown as being the owner.[15] Despite Richard's involvement in trade it is interesting to note that Whites Directory of Suffolk for 1844 lists him as "Gent, Earsham Street".

In 1844 Robert Burstall is given as the miller,[16] presumably he was the tenant of Richard Mann. Robert Burstall is again stated to be the miller here in 1850[17] and in 1855[18]; he also ran Ellingham Mill. During Robert Burstall's occupancy a tragedy occurred at Wainford Mill in 1849. The following report appeared in the Suffolk Mercury on the 4th May of that year — "A little boy under five years of age, has perished at Wainford Mill, in Norfolk (sic), by falling into the hopper, where he was suffocated in the flour. The disaster was discovered by the boy's father who found his son's corpse while emptying the hopper". This could have been Robert Burstall's son but no names are given in the report and so it could equally have been an employee's son.

In 1858 Edward Chaplin is given as a miller at Wainford but he was most likely an employee.[19] James Carley and Chaston are listed as millers and merchants at Wainford Mills in 1864[20] but by the following year the mills were being run by Chaston and Burstall.[21] Next we find Chaston and More occupying the mills in 1869[22] to 1874[23] and they were described as millers and corn merchants. In 1879[24] Thomas More, miller, corn and cake merchant was operating the mills and did so through to 1892[25] when he was utilising steam power, most likely in addition to water power. During the following year, 1893, the mills were demolished and so ended over 800 years of milling at Wainford.[26]

Water power, through the medium of a turbine, was said to be used at the Maltings (dated 1891) adjoining the corn mills at Wainford and the latter are clearly shown on the Ordnance Survey 6 inch map of 1884.

The author of an article on the Waveney Mills (undated) says that as a small boy, when the mill was being dismantled, he was shown a hole in the ground floor of the mill over the water. The hole was made so that Bran could be run direct into the river because there was no trade for it as it cost more for the bags than the Bran was worth![27] As the mill was built over the watercourse, it is obvious that it had an internal water wheel.

The last watermill erected at Wainford was actually situated to the left or south-east of the Mill House (which still exists and is used as offices), and adjoined the smaller brick and slated building attached to the left of the house. It formed part of the Wainford Maltings and Corn Mill complex close to

Wainford Lock. The various buildings close to and adjoining the mill site are now owned and occupied by Messrs. Crisp Malting Ltd., of Gt. Ryburgh, Fakenham, Norfolk.

WAINFORD WATERMILL

1. Albert E. Fairhead, "The Ditchingham that I knew". The Manor of Pirnhow, Chapter II, p.9.
2. Ibid.
3. Ibid.
4. Arundel Castle Archives, Account Book A956.
5. Arundel Castle Archives, MSS MD 511.
6. Sun Fire Insurance Policy No. 396352 (Vol. 264).
7. Sun Fire Insurance Policy No. 409645 (Vol. 273).
8. "Mills Past and Present on the River Waveney", undated article by un-known author, provided by Rank Hovis Ltd.
9. Ipswich Journal, 27th March 1784.
10. Sun Fire Insurance Policy No. 516092 (Vol. 334).
11. Ipswich Journal, 27th May 1786.
12. Sun Fire Insurance Policy No. 549640 (Vol. 356).
13. Pigot & Co.'s Directory.
14. White's Directory.
15. Ibid.
16. Ibid.
17. Hunt & Co.'s Directory.
18. Harrod & Co.'s Directory.
19. Post Office Directory.
20. Harrod & Co.'s Directory.
21. Kelly's Directory.
22. Ibid.
23. White's Directory.
24. Kelly's Directory.
25. Ibid.
26. Ethel Mann, "Old Bungay", 1934, p.20.
27. "Mills Past and Present on the River Waveney", Op. Cit.

Ellingham Watermill, c. 1900. Courtesy of Frank Honeywood.

Ellingham Watermill, staff, c. 1940. Left to right, Mr H. Stone, Mr Stone, Mr D Tilney, Miss Mary Stone, Mr E Gilbert, Major Ellis (manager and nephew of A E Walker), Mr L Seaman, Mr A E Walker, Mr Dot Hood, Mr F Burrows Snr., Mr F. Burrows Jnr. and Mr Sid Hood. Courtesy of Mrs L Seaman.

Ellingham Watermill, Norfolk

NGR TM365917

THE earliest reference to this mill occurs in c.1200 in an Agreement between Alexander de Kerkeby and William de Hales that Alexander should pledge to William his part of the mill at Ellingham with easements in water and fishing … for a term of 20 years from Christmas after the ordination of John Bishop of Norwich for 80 marks of silver with which William shall acquit Alexander of debt and interest of the Jews of Norwich. (John de Grey, Bishop of Norwich was consecrated on 4th September 1200).[1]

There is a mention of Ellingham Mill in an Indenture assessing the Lockage at the Bungay Navigation dated September 7, 1672.[2] Again this mill is cited in "an order by the Commissioners" from which "it appears there is a difference between the Exors. And the Heirs at-law of Mr. Hammond late of Ellingham in the Co. of Norfolk as to which of them the estate in a Water Mill at Ellingham aforesaid should belong. Dat 1676".[3]

In 1772 the miller was Lincoln Matchett and on the 1st January of that year he insured his "Water Corn Mills under one Roof with the going geers belonging situate as aforesaid (i.e., Ellingham in the County of Norfolk), brick timber and tiled not exceeding £1200. Utensils and stock therein £300".[4]

The presence of Ellingham Mill at this period is confirmed by Faden's Map of Suffolk of 1783. It also appears on the earlier maps of Kirby 1736 and Bowen 1760. On Hodskinson's Map of the same date a windmill is shown against the north-west side of the watermill and a further windmill due north of it. Faden's Map of Norfolk of 1797 shows it as a "flourmill" as do Bryant's Maps of 1824, 1825 and 1826, while the 1884 Ordnance Survey 6" map shows a cornmill.

The actual owner of Ellingham Mill in 1788 was Michael Hicks. He was mentioned in connection with an Arbitration concerning differences between Matthias Kerrison, the owner of the Navigation, and the occupiers of this mill.

Parson Woodforde mentions this mill in his Diary when he visited the local rector, Mr. Hall, on July 30th 1788. He says, "such a Parsonage House and Gardens and in so low a place, close also to the river which often overflows besides Ellingham Mill so close that the sound of it is continually heard. Such a house and situation I think very far from being agreeable". One cannot but feel that the worthy Parson exercised an element of exaggeration in his complaint of noise from the mill since the Rectory stood some 650 feet to the east and surely nothing of the mill could be heard if the wind was in the east or north-east as it invariably is in this part of the country. During the days of the American War of Independence (1775–83) flour made from this mill was exported to America.[5]

In a document dated April 24, 1798, Jno. and Lincoln Matchett, Millers, are mentioned as being "the then (1791) Occupiers of the Water Mill at Ellingham".[6]

Prior to March 1809 the mill was in the occupation of James Holden. After his death, in the early part of 1809, Ellingham Mill was advertised "To be let for 9 years". The advertisement also stated that the mill "drives four pairs of stones", and enquiries had to be made to Sawer & Williams, Cornfactors, Coopers Row, London.[7]

Robert Burstall (1803–1856) was the miller at Ellingham Mill in 1845[8] and 1846,[9] and he also ran Wainford Mill at this time. He was twice Town Reeve of Bungay, 1845–46 and 1851–52.[10] He was succeeded in 1865 by one William Shearing,[11] who was also a coal merchant. He may have had a short duration in business at Ellingham because William Youngman had taken over by 1868.[12] Henry Youngman, Jnr., is given as the miller the following year, 1869.[13] He also is both a corn miller and coal merchant and he continues at the mill through to April 1907 when he died at the age of 68,[14] a likely total of 38 years at the mill. From around 1892 Trade Directories describe the mill as "Ellingham Patent Roller Mills".

Messrs. George Durrant & Sons, the local auctioneers, offered the property for sale by auction on instructions from the Personal Representatives of the late Mr. Henry Youngman, at the King's Head Hotel, Beccles, on Friday June 14th 1907 "at Three for Four o'clock in the Afternoon, in One Lot". Their sales particulars describe the mill as "The very Valuable Mercantile Property, known as The Ellingham Roller Mills". Some interesting details are given in the sale particulars:-

"The Large Brick & Timber-Built Mills with tiled Roof, fitted with Iron Water Wheel of 17 h.p., Turbine of 8 h.p. and " Trusty" Oil Engine of $12^1/_2$ h.p. by Shillingford, new four years since. Roller Plant for from $1^1/_2$ to 2 Sacks per hour with all the Excellent Machinery for producing the best articles, Pair of French Burr Stones, Capital Granaries, one of which has unloading place for wherries, Coal Store, Stabling for seven horses with loft over, Harness Room, Neat House, Range of Piggeries, Cart Lodges, and Loose Box, Slaughter House with Copper, Barn and other Buildings. A Capital Brick, Plaster and Tiled Dwelling-House containing Dining Room, Drawing Room, Kitchen, two Pantries, Office and Five Bedrooms; Large Well-planted Garden and Orchard, Timber-building used as a Billiard Room; Two Well-Built Brick and Tiled Cottages with Gardens; and Land Planted with about 600 Willow Trees many of which have been planted about 20 years, the whole containing 5 Acres, 3 Roods, 35 Perches or thereabouts. Tenure Freehold."

The sale particulars go on to say that "A Large General Trade has been carried on by the late Mr. Youngman for many years in addition to the Milling Business, and the very valuable Goodwill of the whole is included in the Sale".

According to a report in July 1907, the property was offered for sale but withdrawn. One imagines that, if there were bidders, it failed to reach the reserve price.[15]

The late John Munnings stated that Ellingham Mill was "Once one of the most up-to-date mills on the River until flour milling ceased". He went on to say that this mill was one of the few country mills using plansifters (equipment for sieving flour) instead of centrifugals (devices for dressing flour). He also relates that the mill had two turbines, one fitted about 1895 which was a small German make of 10 h.p. and the other a large Armfield of 90 h.p. Apparently the later turbine proved to be too large and could only be used to full capacity when there was a good head of water and the tail water was low.[16] His information on the turbines does not tie-up with that given in the sale particulars of 1907 although perhaps changes regarding turbines may have been made after 1907.

It seems that Colonel Smith of Ellingham Hall purchased the mill after the auction for, in September 1908, Ellingham Mill was the scene of a tragedy when the miller, Mr. George Butler, described in a contemporary report as the Colonel's tenant, was discovered hanging there. At the inquest it was stated that business worries had brought about a state of depression during which he had taken his own life. A verdict of temporary insanity was recorded.[17]

Colonel Smith sold the mill to William David Walker[18] who was joined in partnership by his brother, Arthur Ernest Walker with E. Youngman as the Manager.[19] After 1912, and through to 1937, they traded as W.D. & A.E. Walker Limited, Ellingham Patent Roller Mills.[20] The company outlived its founders and continued to trade until 1947 when the business was taken over by Hovis Limited.[21] Flour production ceased at Ellingham Mill in 1949 but animal feed production, transferred from Earsham Mill at the same date, continued until 1964 when animal feed production was transferred back to Earsham Mill.[22]

At the date of purchase of the mill, William Walker was already a well established business and civic figure in Bungay. Born at Beccles in 1847, he married Miss Sarah Elizabeth Hope of Manchester in 1873 and lived at Olland

House (now Dunelm) in Lower Olland Street, Bungay. Sarah died in 1888 and Walker then married her sister, Mabel. He had in all 8 children. He was Town Reeve of Bungay for 5 separate terms between 1888 and 1911 and became a J.P. in 1907.[23] He was a staunch supporter of the then Congregational Church.[24]

W.D. & A.E. Walker acquired the navigation rights of the River Waveney between Bungay and Beccles towards the end of the 19th century and they owned and operated a fleet of wherries, including the famous "Albion" built in Oulton Broad in 1898; now preserved and owned by the Norfolk Wherry Trust. Many of their wherries were built at their private yard at Bungay Staithe and others of the fleet were "Hope", "Mayflower", "Eudora" and "Iolanthe". It is interesting to note that whereas it was usual for wherries to be clinker planked, W.D. & A.E. Walker stipulated that "Albion" was to be built carvel planked. The reason for this was that the clinker planked wherries invariably scraped the rough sides of the locks between Bungay and Beccles and it was thought that carvel planking made navigating the locks easier and caused less damage to the wherries. The builder of the "Albion" was Mr. William Brighton and other builders at their private yard were John Winter and George Davey. W.D. & A.E. Walker's wherries were painted bright green and the mastheads were painted with yellow and blue bands.[25]

Not only did W.D. & A.E. Walker own a fleet of wherries which plied between Bungay Staithe and Beccles, Lowestoft and Yarmouth, they also owned Bungay Staithe Maltings (now converted into residential flats). Being the owners of the navigation, they were responsible for the upkeep of the locks at Geldeston (or Shipmeadow), Wainford and Ellingham. However, they were succeeded as navigation owners by Watney, Combe, Reid & Co., in 1919 and in 1920 they sold the wherries "Eudora" and "Iolanthe" to their successors. Six years later these two wherries passed to the General Steam Navigation Company.[26]

Mr. Arthur Ernest Walker who was born in 1852/3 lived at the Tower House, Brundall and visited Ellingham Mill once a week, usually Thursday mornings. He arrived in either a maroon or navy coloured chauffeur driven motor car, the chauffeur's uniform matching the colour of the car. During his visitations, children were not allowed to play in front of the mill and if they met Mr. Walker they had to curtsey![27]

Mrs. Leslie Seaman of Attleborough also recalls that on occasions when a new lot of wheat was ground, her mother Mrs. Fred Burrows, made and baked a batch of white and brown bread for Mr. Ernest Walker to sample. Mrs. Seaman went to the mill cottage in 1916 at the age of three when her father, Mr. Fred Burrows, joined the mill staff. Her husband, Mr. Leslie Seaman worked in the mill from 1930 at the age of 18, until he was called up for War Service in 1941. Her brother Mr. Fred Burrows, Jnr., also worked at the mill. When Mr. Leslie Seaman started at the mill his wages were 22s 6d (112.5p) per week and his work included carrying sacks of grain up to the granary. In 1935

A horse-drawn trolley outside Ellingham Mill, c. 1940, with, left to right, Mr L Seaman, Mr Dot Hood, Mr Sid Hood and Mr Horace Neal.

Ellingham Watermill and Mill House, 1990. D F Pluck.

Mr. Seaman made an appointment to see Mr. Ernest Walker to ask for an increase in his wages as he was about to marry Miss Burrows. Asked why he wanted an increase he informed Mr. Walker that he was getting married. Whereupon Mr. Walker asked him how much he wanted. He informed him 25s 0d (125p) per week. Mr. Walker then asked him if he thought he was worth it! The reply was obviously satisfactory and he was granted the increase and married.[28]

Another employee at Ellingham Mill, Mr. Sidney Hood, retired in 1977 after 51 years service in the Agricultural Merchants Trade. He started his working life with W.D. & A.E. Walker Limited, spending the first few months on a farm at Ellingham, then he moved to Bungay Staithe where he helped to look after pigs. At about the age of 18 he moved to Ellingham Mill from where he delivered goods by horse and trolley for a year going seven or eight miles on a journey. Later he also worked at Earsham Mill and as a schoolboy well remembered the wherries on the Waveney, indeed he helped to unload the last one to come up which was the "Albion". He also vividly remembers the floods at Ellingham and during the 1940's he spent a whole night at the mill making sure it did not become flooded, accompanied by a number of rats! On another occasion he ran a race with a "mate" of his at Ellingham Mill, each carrying 17 stone of maize on their backs over a distance of 100 yards![29]

After a long and successful business career Mr. A.E. Walker died at the age of 93 and shortly after his death the mill was taken over by Hovis Limited. Before Hovis took over, the firm that operated Ellingham Mill was known as Walker Marston. There is an illustration of the mill in existence and on the front elevation are the words *WALKER MARSTON MILL*. Walker Marston Limited, Ellingham, Suffolk (sic) was listed as one of the Hovis Provender Mills and as a subsidiary.[30] It seems that Charles Marston got to know that Hovis were interested in taking over the mill and he "assisted" in the matter by taking a direct interest himself thus facilitating the requisition by Hovis and at the same time forestalling anyone else with a similar intention. No doubt the move was not to Charles Marston's own disadvantage.

When animal feed production ceased in 1964, Ellingham Mill was put on the market. And so in November 1964, the mill, mill house, a single-storey brick warehouse (built 1946), stores, garages and brick-built thatched barn, with an area of "nearly four acres and 600 ft. mill stream" was offered for sale by Hillier, Parker, May & Rowden of London in conjunction with Arnold Son & Hockley of Norwich. At that time its use was stated to be a factory and warehouse.[31] A sale by private treaty was arranged but did not materialise and in May 1965 the property was again put up for sale by private treaty at an asking price of £13,250 for the whole or £12,000 if the water rights were excluded. The property remained on the market through to 1966 but a buyer was not forthcoming.

The same Agents then submitted the property to Public Auction in six lots,

"At Low Reserves", on Wednesday 6th July 1966, at the King's Head Hotel, Bungay at 3 p.m. They described the property as being formerly occupied by Messrs. Vitovis Limited, and being surplus to their requirements is being offered for sale. There was a stipulation that the purchasers of any of the lots would enter into a covenant to the effect that the property would NOT be used *"FOR PROVENDER MILLING, ANIMAL FOOD MANUFACTURE, CORN DEALING OR PROCESSING OR FERTILIZER MANUFACTURE OR SALE"*. Lot 1 was the Mill House, Lot 2 The Office Accommodation, Lot 3 The Warehouse, Lot 4 A Small Granary, Lot 5 Large Barn and Garage Premises and Lot 6 The Main Mill with Mill Stream, Sluice Gate and Valuable Water rights. The Mill was connected to the Warehouse by an overhead conveyor and the Vendors undertook to dismantle it "before completion of the purchase and at their own expense". They never did and it remained in situ. The overhead conveyor was obviously erected when the warehouse was built and it runs from the apex of the south gable end of the mill, where a lucam was removed, down to the warehouse at an angle of approximately 65°. The conveyor facilitated the removal of corn, etc., from the mill to the warehouse and vice versa and being completely enclosed, goods were protected from the elements. There was a plate attached to the overhead conveyor which read:

ROWSON, DREW & CLYDESDALE LTD.,
MECHANICAL HANDLING ENGINEERS
225 UPPER THAMES ST. LONDON, EC4.

In the Special Conditions of Sale, No. 7 recites that "The Title to the property shall commence with a Conveyance on sale dated the 15th day of July 1907 made between Ernest George Youngman of the one part and William David Hawker of the other part".

All the lots were sold at auction with the exception of Lot 3. The results of the sale were as follows:-
Lot 1: The Mill House to Mr. P.B. Wordley of Norton for £3,050.00
Lot 2: The Office Accommodation to Mr. P.B. Wordley for £775.00.
Lot 3: The Warehouse was withdrawn at £2,250.00
Lot 4: A Small Granary to Mr. P.B. Wordley for £750.00.
Lot 5: Large Barn and Garage Premises to Mr. B.C. Hutson of Godmanchester for   £1,650.00.
Lot 6: The Main Mill to Mr. B.C. Hutson for £3,000.00.[32]

Later, it seems the Warehouse was sold and then offered on lease at £250 per annum the tenant paying rates and cost of repairs.

After the sale of the various parts of the property in 1966, considerable alterations were effected as well as restoration. In the summer of 1970 Ellingham Mill was again sold through the Norwich Office of Alfred Savill,

Curtis and Henson. It had by then "been converted to provide four flats, of which the main one was offered with vacant possession". "A price of more than £15,000.00 was paid for the property, which has 400ft. of river frontage".[33] Over the years the mill has been added to and various alterations made, thus altering the various facades not inconsiderably. When a comparison is made between an early photograph of the mill taken around the turn of the century or very early in the present century, and illustrations of more recent date, it will be readily appreciated how the mill has changed. The early photograph shows eight windows in the front elevation and no lucam whereas today there are sixteen windows plus a dormer window and a lucam with another window.

The roof line has also been altered such that a gable has been inserted in which is incorporated the front lucam. The mill was also extended at the southern end in brick. When a comparison is made between photographs taken of the rear of the mill c.1964 and 1970, it will be seen that the rear lucam has also been removed (this was used for the loading and unloading of the wherries) and windows have been altered and enlarged. The Mill therefore possessed three lucams at one time, on the front, rear and southern end.

The Mill was originally built in traditional timber framing under a pantiled roof and on a stone base. The exterior is clad in the familiar white painted weatherboarding. The Mill house which adjoins the Mill at its northern end, is also a timber framed building with a pantiled roof and with attractive gothic windows. It probably dates from the late medieval period although it was refronted in the early 19th century.

At present the mill is divided vertically into three residential units. The northern section is occupied with The Mill House and incorporates an artist's studio and gallery. The warehouse was at one time used as a book store.

Planning consent was granted to demolish part of the warehouse and to convert the remainder into a house.[34] The black conveyor linking the mill to the warehouse has been removed, the warehouse partly demolished with the remainder converted into a residence.

The property is situated in The Ellingham Mill Conservation Area and the Mill and adjoining house are both Listed Grade II under the Town & Country Planning Acts. They are privately owned and not opened to the public.

ELLINGHAM WATERMILL

1. The Norfolk Collection of the Antiquaries, N.R.O., MC44/1.
2. S.R.O. (L) Acc 187/1.
3. Ibid.
4. Sun Fire Insurance Policy No. 306301 (Vol. 210).
5. "Mills Past and Present on the River Waveney", article by unknown author and undated, from Rank Hovis Ltd.
6. S.R.O. (I) HA 85/3116/24.

7. The Times, March 20, 1809.
8. Whites Directory.
9. Post Office Directory.
10. John Harris "The Town Reeves of Bungay, 1725–1986, A Study of a unique and ancient office and those who have occupied it". 1986.
11. Kelly's Directory.
12. J.G. Harrod's Directory.
13. Kelly's Directory.
14. The Miller, 6th May 1907.
15. The Miller, 1st July, 1907.
16. John Munnings, "The Passing of the Country Miller and His Mill, Rivers Stour and Waveney", unpublished article, c.1970.
17. The Miller, 5th October 1908.
18. Mr. D.V.C. Walker of Bungay, Suffolk.
19. Kelly's Directory.
20. Kelly's Directories.
21. Mr. Frank E. Cannell of Bungay, Suffolk.
22. Ibid.
23. John Harris, Op. Cit.
24. Ibid.
25. Robert Malster, "Wherries and Waterways", 1971, p.p. 23, 31, 52, 77, 121, 122 and 123.
26. Ibid.
27. Mrs. Leslie Seaman, (née Burrows) of Attleborough, Norfolk.
28. Ibid.
29. The Journal, Friday July 1st, 1977.
30. A.H. Dence, Esq., J.P., "The Hovis Jubilee", A Brief record of the Company's history between 1898–1948. Privately printed 1948. Mr. Dence was chairman of Hovis Limited.
31. The Estates Gazette, 14th November 1964.
32. Eastern Daily Press, 7th July 1966.
33. Country Life, December 17th/24th 1970.
34. Eastern Daily Press, 10th June 1989.

Geldeston Watermill, Norfolk

NGR TM390909

Little seems to be known about this mill, indeed when making enquiries people seemed surprised that a mill ever existed by the lock.

It is shown on A. Bryant's map of 1824/5 as "Shipmeadow Locks Mill". If one lived on the Norfolk side of the River Waveney then the mill was known as Geldeston Mill but if you resided on the Suffolk side, it was referred to as Shipmeadow Mill.[1]

James Stark (1794–1859) of the Norfolk School of Painters, produced a painting entitled "Shipmeadow Lock (on the Waveney)". The painting was engraved and a plate is included in the book entitled "Scenery of the Rivers of Norfolk comprising The Yare, The Waveney and The Bure. From pictures painted by James Stark, with Historical and Geological Descriptions by J.W. Robberds Jnr., Esq. Norwich; Printed by John Stacy, Old Haymarket, London; Published by Moon, Boys and Graves, Waterloo Place, Pall Mall; and Jennings and Chaplin, 62 Cheapside, MDCCCXXXIV (1834)".[2]

Obviously James Stark painted his picture of Shipmeadow Lock sometime prior to the publication of this book but the mill does not appear on the First Edition of the Ordnance Survey 1 inch map of 1838, so presumably the mill must have disappeared shortly before the survey was carried out for this map.

From the contents of a document dated 23rd July 1785[3] and quoted in full on page 21, it would not seem unreasonable to conclude that this mill was built about 1785. If this is so, then it had a somewhat short life, something in the region of only 50 years. The reason for this brief span is difficult to ascertain or understand. Perhaps the fact that Shipmeadow/Geldeston mill is located away from the major corn growing area and nearer to large areas of grazing marshes resulted in trade being insubstantial and irregular. After all the building of this mill was encouraged because it would "be of real use by drawing off water" and not, it is to be noted, primarily to produce corn or grist for the locality. There were of course periods of acute depression during the first part of the nineteenth century, brought about by the Napoleonic Wars

(1799–1815), and these circumstances may well have been a contributing factor to the closure of this mill.

James Stark's painting depicts the Lock, with a Wherry passing through, the lock-keeper's cottage through the trees and part of the mill in the background above trees. From this painting the mill appears to be timber framed, weatherboarded and on a brick base or footings under a pantiled roof. It has a lucam, similarly constructed, and with straight brackets. The mill seems to be sited near the north-west end or side of the cottage. It is fair to assume that Geldeston or Shipmeadow mill was a flour mill. The cottage had a beer licence by 1768.[4]

When the writer visited the Lock on the 29th September 1988, there were no apparent remains of the mill except perhaps a small amount of brickwork, laid herringbone pattern in the footpath to the west of the cottage, now The Lock Public House. The latter was being extended at the time and a Notice on the downstream side of the iron footbridge reads:

"End of Tidal Navigation".

GELDESTON WATERMILL

1. Mr. A.F. Jermy of Bungay.
2. Norwich Record Office
3. S.R.O. (I) HA85/3116/657.
4. David Alderton & John Booker, "The Batsford Guide to the Industrial Archaeology of East Anglia," 1980.

Oakley Mill and Mill House, River Dove, 1983. The mill comprises the left-hand section of the building up to the two very small square first-floor windows. It is now incorporated into the residence. P C J Dolman.

Part of the premises of E H Knights & Sons at Harleston, Norfolk in 1989, and now demolished. D F Pluck.

Two wooden templates at Messrs. E H Knights & Sons. Left, double gear, right, bevel gear. D F Pluck.

Oakley Watermill, River Dove, Suffolk

NGR TM171770

There are, of course, various tributaries to the River Waveney, but the principal one is the River Dove which joins the main river at a point about half a mile or so east of Billingford (NGR TM177784). A watermill has existed on the River Dove for some considerable time and was situated only a mile or so from the Waveney. As far as is known, this was the only watermill on this tributary. This being so, it was thought appropriate to include this particular mill in these notes as also being of interest.

In Anglo-Saxon times the mill and other property here was owned by The Anglian Bishop Theodred. Then at the time of the Domesday Survey, 1086, Robert Malet (under fee of the Abbot of Bury), held a small estate in Oakley consisting of seven acres of land, a mill, a rouncy, 2 beasts and 5 sheep, at an annual value of 20s.

From the time of the Norman Conquest the mill would have passed to the "de Hoo's", "the Bacons" and "the Buctons". In 1400, as a result of John Cornwallis, the son of a Sheriff of London, marrying Philippa Bucton of Oakley, land on the Oakley side of the River Dove including the mill, would have passed into Cornwallis' ownership and remained so for the next 423 years. Land on the Hoxne side of the river in due time passed to the Maynard family.[1]

The watermill is shown on Kirby's map of Suffolk, 1736, on Bowen's map of Suffolk, 1760; also on Faden's map of Suffolk 1783. On both maps a windmill is also shown thereon standing within 200 yards of and to the north-east of the former. Robert Cook was the tenant and miller in 1780 and on the 7th January of that year he insured his "furniture in his dwellinghouse and Water Millhouse in one building, timber and plaster built and tiled and thatched, situate in Oakley aforesaid £70. On trade in the same £180. On the mills and going geers of £50".[2] He was in all probability a tenant of the Cornwallis estate.

After the death of the 2nd Marquis Cornwallis, Matthias Kerrison of Bungay, purchased the Cornwallis and Maynard properties in 1823. On the amalgamation of these estates, the River Dove ceased functioning as an estate boundary but simply ran through the new and larger property. Matthias Kerrison died on the 12th April 1827, at Bungay (see notes under Bungay Watermill) and his son, Major-General Sir Edward Kerrison, Bart., of Brooke, Norfolk, inherited the estate.[3]

Quite when the watermill ceased functioning is not known. However on the Ordnance Survey 1 inch map of 1837 (first edition) and the 25 inch map of 1904, the mill building is named "Laundry". So at some stage a conversion was effected. On the 1926 edition of the Ordnance Survey 25 inch map the building is again renamed, this time it is designated "Parklands". On the latest edition of the 25 inch map it is called "The Old Mill". At some point in its life the building was further converted into private residential accommodation and added to the existing house, probably sometime after 1921. The whole building is now a private residence and it is also a Listed Building Grade II under the Town & Country Planning Acts.

OAKLEY WATERMILL

1. Information kindly supplied by Eric D. King in his letter to the County Solicitor at Ipswich in connection with Public Footpaths in the Parish of Oakley, dated 28th April 1988.
2. Royal Exchange Fire Insurance Policy No. 77219.
3. Eric D. King, Op. Cit.

CONCLUSION

What is all knowledge too but recorded experience,
and a product of history; of which, therefore,
reasoning and belief, no less than action and passion,
are essential materials.

Thomas Carlyle, 1795–1881

Prior to the Industrial Revolution, the most reliable means of transport in most areas of the country was provided by River Navigation. As has been related in previous pages, the River Waveney supplied the means for water-borne transport from Yarmouth upstream to Bungay. Prior to the middle of the eighteenth century improvements were made to river navigations; then between 1750 and 1850 turnpike roads were created. Later the railways were to exert their influence, the sections between Tivetshall, Harleston, Bungay, Beccles and Lowestoft being opened on the 1st December 1855 through to the 2nd March 1863. Inevitably, the then Waveney Valley Railway gradually appropriated the transportation of goods from the Navigation causing the latter to decline although it did not close until 1934.

The River and Navigation, perhaps more so in the earlier days, affected the general development as well as the lives of many people living in the towns and villages near at hand. Certain crafts and trades became established mainly because of the river. Watermills and boatbuilding are prime examples.

The importance of the watermill itself cannot be over-emphasised. It was an important adjunct to a predominantly agricultural zone and this facilitated the production of a considerable quantity of flour from wheat grown close at hand.

It is regrettable that of the original fifteen watermills in the Waveney Valley, only six survive and none of those have been restored to working order. Three of the remaining mills have been converted to residential use, one partly to residential use, one to business use, one is derelict and in the case of the sixth restitution could possibly be effected as its waterwheel remains in situ together with a certain amount of machinery.

A visit to a working watermill is a very interesting and rewarding experience.

In the adjoining county of Suffolk, there is a restored watermill at Pakenham which is open to the public at certain times. It is situated about six miles north-east of Bury St. Edmunds. Pakenham is, as far as is known, the only Parish in which there is both a working watermill and windmill, an unique situation at the present time although commonplace in years gone by.

There are today, in various parts of the country, many mills powered by water or wind which have been restored to working order. A list of these mills together with days and times of opening to the public can be obtained from the Wind & Watermill Section of The Society for the Protection of Ancient Buildings, 37 Spital Square, London E1 6DY.

Knowledge is of two kinds. We know a subject ourselves, or we know where we can find informa-tion upon it.

Samuel Johnson, 1709–1784

Appendix A
Hoxne Watermill

Schedules contained in a Counterpart Lease of July 1855
(S.R.O. (I) HA/68/484/673)

"THE SECOND SCHEDULE referred to in the above written Indenture being machinery at the Steam and Water Mills belonging to Sir Edward Clarence Kerrison and formerly ... Edward Kerrison Baronet deceased ... Water Mill – Oak mud Sills – four staple posts – cap sill and all the framing and ... foundation – A new cast iron Water Wheel shaft two cast iron plummer blocks ... and fixed to new oak sills two cast iron shifting blocks fitted to ditto and two brasses – A new Water Wheel ... Iron rings and iron arms attached forty eight oak floats drumboards and starts hung and fitted to shaft with iron keys – A new cast iron watergate with iron rabbets purchase shaft – Iron plummer blocks – two purchase wheels – purchase pinion and three horned Crank A new Cast iron pit wheel with iron arms – Iron grapples And No. 114 iron cogs fixed and hung to iron shaft with eight iron keys – A new cast iron upright shaft with three bearings two plummer blocks bolts and brasses to each cast iron bridging box set screws and fastenings bolts large convex step brass and collar A cast iron crown nut with thirty nine cogs pitched trimmed and bored cut fitted and hung to upright shaft with shifting reed one large key wedge and raising screws A cast iron spur wheel hung and fitted to upright shaft with iron keys and geared with one hundred and thirty six wood cogs three cast iron stone nuts each with nineteen iron cogs and each bored out and fitted to tap spindle and make to rack up three set irons with centre bars maces and feeding irons Three cast iron neck boxes each fitted with three brasses three sliding wedges two wrought iron collars and bolts three cast iron bridging pots each with set screws and fastening bolts two iron slide pots and three step brasses four cast lifting irons fitted with wrought lifting and purchase irons three sets of lighter screws with brass and iron collars three mahogany poppets and collars All the timber for Stone Hurst Meal trough and spouts and cases round the same – One pair of new four feet french stones Two pair of ditto rebuilt – each fitted up with curving and iron vats wood bearers – hopper and shoe and shoe brass – A cast iron flywheel hung and fitted to upright shaft with eight iron keys and geared with seventy two wood cogs keyed in A cast iron horizontal shaft with two iron plummer blocks each fitted with shifting brass set screws and bolts a cast bevil pinion with sixteen iron cogs pitched trimmed and bored out hung and fitted to shaft with one key a thirty six inch drum rigger with iron sides each bored out Flour machine fitted with mahogany cylinder wrought iron barrel and brushes cast iron brays plummer blocks bolts and brasses To (sic) cast iron conical wheels each with iron cogs pitched trimmed and bored out – wrought iron horizontal spindle plummer blocks and brasses – One fifteen inch iron rigger and small hopper leading to wheat bin floor Flour bolting Mill fitted with reel beaters and small hopper leading to wheat bin floor one pair of iron conical wheels with iron cogs pitched trimmed and bored out wrought iron horizontal spindle plummer blocks and brasses and one twelve inch iron rigger One eight foot six inch jumper sixteen inches wide with flour frames poppets and brays as fixed One wrought iron crank spindle plummer blocks bolts and brasses and iron driving rigger One eighteen inch and one thirty inch iron rigger for hoisting tackle with fir barrel iron gudgeon and brass bearings purchase shaft and rigger all the brays and poppets as fixed three cast iron running pullies with wrought iron spindle Steam Engine – A six horse power high pressure and condensing steam engine – together with all the feed pipes hot and cold water pumps wrought iron boiler and brickwork as fixed A mercurial gauge and about fifteen rounds of Quicksilver cast iron crank shaft two plummer blocks and foundation plates and bolts two cast iron spur wheels each with iron cogs – a cast iron horizontal shaft with coupling joints five plummer blocks bolts and brasses cast iron bevil pinion with thirty five iron cogs pitched trimmed and bored out and made to slide out with proper clutch cast iron bevil wheel hung to upright shaft with wrought iron keys and geared with seventy two wooden cogs keyed in – Out Door New Cast Iron Grating and Wood plank on oaken timber framed sluice with two cast iron flood gates – two cast iron flashes and wrought iron handles two wooden rolls – two cast iron ratchet wheels and iron catches …

THE THIRD SCHEDULE referred to by the above written Indenture being fixtures and machinery at the Steam and Water Corn Mills the property of Sir Edward Clarence Kerrison Baronet and purchased by him of William Buttrum the late tenant of the said Mills in March One thousand eight hundred and fifty four – In the Water Mill – Lower Floor – four pairs of $1^1/_4$ inch panelled shutters with joints and iron fastenings Wood frame for eight feet six inch Jumper with three Wood shackles and screw bolts to the same Stone Floor – One new four feet french bed stone as fixed to No. 2 Wrought iron guide bars and cast iron presses roll with bush brasses purchase rigger and lines to the same thirty three feet of scantling for guide posts as fixed Wheat Floor – five ledge shutters to Wheat floor windows five hundred and sixteen feet of 5/8 deal partition on wheat floor – meal bin and pastry wrought and rabbitted three hundred and ninety six feet of studs rails bearers &c for the same two hundred and seventy seven feet of half inch casing on outside studding and round sack tackling wrought and rabbitted two small sash frames and glass in partitions two large grist hoppers and one meal hopper with studs and bearers spout leading from Stage to Jumper two ledge doors 2ft 6in: by 6 foot 6 inch with Joints and Buttons five slips board fifteen feet inch thick – Stage Floor – Ninety five feet of inch flooring over pastry and wheat bin and one hundred and thirty two feet of Joists $2^1/_2$ by 6 and seventy two feet of inch flooring on stage $8^1/_2$ feet of 3/4 inch partition six small wheat hoppers and lips attached to wheat floor – In the Steam Mill – Lime to new brick end and foundations to receive the Stone hurst – Nails for laying three square of floor and joist two cast iron window frames 3ft. 2in: by 3ft. 6in. glazed – Glass door and frame 6ft. by 2ft. 10in. glazed 2ft. 3in. by 3 feet Two foundation bolts 3 feet long one inch diameter horizontal cast iron shaft with clutch attached and bearings turned and 1/2 clutch bored and turned to relative shaft A cast iron plummer block with brasses and screw bolts to the same two cast iron mortice counter wheels geared with seventy two cogs each hung with four iron keys two cast iron bevil stone nuts twenty four cogs each bored and pitched and trimmed complete and reed way out four foot four inch cast iron drum $5^1/_2$ inch wide turned sole and edge bored and hung with one key wood hand rail bottom sill and twenty three 1/

2 inch bars 3ft. 6in. long – round drum pit – two cast iron bridge trees and mill head screws – two cast iron bridging potts Centre Pots and step brasses and fastening bolts to the same two bevil wheels and two pinions – two cast iron lighter bars with screws for regulating stone with spindle plummer blocks and hand wheels – two sets of hoisting irons for hoisting nuts out of gear – two cast iron stone spindles turned with reeds let in for stone nuts Stone Floor – Two cast iron stone boxes with brasses bored and adjusting keys and screws at back Centre bars and Maces and two damsels two pair of 3ft. 10 in: french stones two Curbles – two Sheet iron Vats with bearers hoppers and shoes – forty feet of $1^1/_4$ in: boards – partition in offal room – twenty seven feet of studs – 5/8 partition 8ft. long by 5ft. 6 in: forty two feet of studs – Forty seven and a half feet of $1^1/_4$ by 9 inch slip boards – ten inch wood stock lock – 3/4 inch ledge door 3 feet by 4 feet 9 inch with joints 3/4 inch Elmpipe leading to Jumper – two meal Spouts with mahogany lips and brass slips – two meal troughs partition and studs in front of Cog pit – four pannel sash door and jambs in front of Cog pit – 7feet 6in: of Brickwork by 1 foot 6 inch: one brick. Out Doors – Oaken broad step ladder fifteen steps and three bolts to ditto – Dwellinghouse – Broad step ladder eleven steps eighteen inches wide 3/4 in: ledge door 6 feet by 2 feet 6 in: joints and laten ledge shutter 4 feet by 4 feet 6 inches to back – Kitchen window …
Signed by George Godbold and John Chase

NOTE: Being part of a legal document there is no punctuation.

Appendix B
Syleham Watermill

Sale Particulars (undated but pre-1899) of George Durrant & Sons, Auctioneers, Valuers, and Estate Agents, Harleston, Beccles and Bungay.

SUFFOLK

Particulars of a
VALUABLE FREEHOLD
MERCANTILE ESTATE
known as the
SYLEHAM DRABBETT FACTORY AND
FLOUR MILLS,

Situate close to the Village of Brockdish, and about 3 miles from the Market Town and Railway Station of Harleston, Norfolk (Waveney Branch G.E.R.)
With Superior

FAMILY RESIDENCE

Having extensive kitchen and Pleasure Gardens and Grounds, Glass Houses, TWO COTTAGES, Cart and Nag Stabling, Coach Houses, Outbuildings, Offices, &c., and about

19 ACRES

of Good PASTURE and ALLOTMENT LAND all bordering on the River Waveney.

For upwards of 60 years successfully carried on by the Proprietors the late Messrs. H. & C. Warne, and at present in the occupation of Messrs. E.A. Holmes & Co., whose lease expires on October 11th 1899, when possession will be given.

The Premises comprise:- Part brick, and part boarded and tiled 2 storey

DRABBETT FACTORY & FLOUR MILLS,

104ft. x 150ft., having Forge House; Boiler and Engine House with boiler and 16-h.p. horizontal Steam Engine by E.R. & F. Turner; Coal House; Shaft 48ft. High; Drabbett Dressing House,

168

23ft. by 28ft.; Store House 15ft. 6in. by 15ft. 6in.; New Weaving
Shed 32ft. by 19ft.; Main Weaving Mill 104ft. by 50ft. well lighted
in sides and roof; Clay and Tiled Dyeing Shed 45ft. by 18ft. 6in.;
Finishing Room 26ft. 6in. by 12ft. with Pressing Room over;
Sewing Room 43ft 6in. by 17ft. 6in.; Yarn Chamber 18ft. by 13ft
6in. with doors to road and staircase; Starching Room 53ft. by
51ft. including Winding and Warping Chambers; Calender*
House 20ft. 6in. by 19ft. 6in.; Warehouse 16ft. by 14ft.; Main
Warehouse 34ft. by 18ft. 6in.; Private Office adjoining 18ft. by
12ft.
ANCIENT TOLL HOUSE and Gate, with the right of Toll over
Private Bridge and Road (the tenant for the time being, keeping
the road in repair).

THE GRIST MILL

With Corn and Stone Floors, three pairs of 4ft. French Burr
Stones driven by powerful water wheel and auxiliary steam
power.
On the opposite side of the road are Brick, Stud and Tiled Ready-
made Clothing Department 65ft. by 21ft., lofty and well-lighted;
Drying Shed with Chamber adjoining; Store and Warehouses
75ft. in length with Cutting-out Room over, 32ft. 6in. by 21ft.
Hay House; Lean-to Coach House, Harness and Coal Houses;
Range of Nag Stabling, with 4 Loose Boxes, and Hay and Corn
House adjoining; Stable Yard, Water Tank; Cart Stable with
Harness House and Loft; Large Coach House, with 2 Folding
Doors. Open Cart Lodge, Lean-to Shed and Privy.
At a short distance is Clay and Thatched

COTTAGE

with Outbuildings and Gardens, Allotment and Paddock.
In the River is a Private island approached by Rustic Bridge, on
which is a Summer-house and Boat House

THE RESIDENCE

built of Red Brick and Tiled, of pleasing elevation, is situated at
a convenient distance, stands in its own Gardens and Grounds
sloping down to the river, amongst some fine ornamental tim-
bers and trees.
It contains-Entrance Hall with principal staircase; Dining Room
22ft. by 14ft. to bay window, with Oak Mantel and Stove; Drawing
Room 22ft. by 14ft. with Marble Mantel and Stove, Cellar, Pantry,
Closets, Larder, Dairy, W.C., Kitchen with Cooking Range,
Oven, Pump supplying Spring Water, Sink, Cook's Closet and
Back Entrance, Housekeeper's Room with Stove, Cupboards
and Dressers, Day and Night Nurseries, Staircase, Landing and
Passages leading to 3 principal and 4 Attic or Secondary Bed-
rooms conveniently arranged and fitted with stoves and closets,
Box Room.
Upper Kitchen Garden well-planted and stocked with choicest

---

* A machine with rollers for finishing the surface of cloth, paper, etc., by combined moisture, heat
  and pressure.

varieties of fruit trees and bushes, 2 Vineries, Cucumber House
with heating apparatus. Potting House, Tool House and Fruit
Chamber, Low Kitchen Garden and Orchard.
A small and compact set of Clay, Boarded and Corrugated Iron
Roofed

FARM BUILDINGS

comprising Neat House, Piggeries, Fowl Houses, &c., and several
Enclosures of Fine Pasture and Arable Land, the whole containing

19a.   3r.   11p.

OUTGOINGS

Property Tax (Schedule A) Assessment —

House and Buildings		£196	18s.	0d.
Cottages		£16	10s.	0d.
Land Tax (paid)			19s.	9d.

Poor Rate Assessments —

Land gross £17	net	£16	10s.
House and Buildings Gross £146	net	£110	
Cottages gross £11	net	£8	10s.

Tithe Rent Charge (last payment)   £1   7s.   6d.

The Estate will be let (with option of purchase) at October 11th,
1899.

N.B. — The Mill and Factory are now in full work and employ
from 80 to 100 hands, and the present tenants are willing to treat
with intending hirers or purchasers for the taking over of the
business as a going concern, also for the goodwill, Book Debts,
Stock-in-Trade, Machinery, &c., &c.

The returns based on an average of the past 3 years are about
£9,000 per annum.

Schedule of Fixtures and Effects at Syleham Mill, the property of
E.A. Holmes & Co., which the Landlords or their ingoing Tenant
will have the option of taking by Valuation.

MILL — Warping machine, cotton winding machine, dressing
knife, grinding machine, cutting-out ma-
chine, 12 looms as fixed with belting,
shafting, drums, &c.

SEWING ROOM — 24 sewing machines, 3 button machines, all
benches, shafting, pulleys, &c., the treadle
sewing and knitting machines.

NEW DRESSING ROOM — The fixtures and stove.

BARKWAY'S ROOM — Stove.

BARN — Fire engine.

MEADOW — Lawn tennis house and railing with posts.

HARNESS HOUSE — Stove.

In addition to the above all Stock, Fittings and Effects in and
about the premises can be left for valuation of desired.

Schedule of Fixtures, &c., at Syleham Mill, the property of
E.A. Holmes & Co., for Valuation to the Tenant.

OFFICE — 10 ft. of shelving.

LITTLE WAREHOUSE — All shelving and staging, table with drawer and oil cloth cover, deal table, iron stove with flue pipe, scales and weights, small steps.

CALENDERING HOUSE — Rack and rough shelving.

WAREHOUSE — Shelving over side door and near window, spline and hooks with shield, counter with drawer, 13ft. steps to loft, screw press.

DAMPING HOUSE — All stands, brushing machine with 20 in. iron pulley and strap.

MILL — Knife grinding machine, lathe, iron pump with pipe, copper furnace and lid, 8 loom beams, 50 loom rods.

WAREHOUSE NEXT COP-HOUSE— 50 ft. staging on supports, 7ft. 6in. counter, rack.

DRESSING ROOM — 2 dressing machines as fixed with 30ft. shafting, 2 pulleys, spare emery roller, knife and bed, 6ft. 6in. dresser, stool, clock, 6ft. staging.

SINGEING HOUSE — 10ft. staging, 15ft. spline, steps.

BOILER AND COAL HOUSES — Privy next blacksmith's shop.

STARCHING CHAMBER — Vat.

FLOUR MILL — Working parts for looms, castings and fittings.

DYE HOUSE — 4 stagings.

SEWING ROOM — Two flat heating stoves on zinc stands with flue pipes, 123ft. benching on supports.

CUTTING ROOM — Ladder to clock, all shelving.

OLD DRYING ROOM — Shelving, "Carron" with flue pipe.

STABLE — 30ft. railing, manger and rack renewed.

YARD — Water cistern re-lined and renewed.

DRYING SHED — The steps to same, spline gate and rails.

HOUSE

Note — The Fixtures in and about the House as taken by Mr. Holmes upon entry at Mr. J.L. Moore's Valuation are not here mentioned as they appear set out in the award.

Appendix C
Needham Watermill

Schedule contained in an Indenture dated the 20th February 1915.

Stage Floor Scale beam and scales. 19 stones of weights. Gate pulley and pulling in cord sack hoist and chain. Sack barrow. Flour scoop and broom. Ten stave ladder. Wood hopper and spout to conveyor.

Silk Floor Flour centrifugal driving machine. Flour dressing machine. The reel 18 feet long in wood case with shutters and band conveyor Silk clothing for above in five sheets Nos: 000, 6, 7, 8 and 9, 5 feet of $1^1/_2$ inch shafting. Two plummer blocks and brasses, Pulley 12 inches by 4 inches, Pulley 12 inches by $2^1/_2$ inches. Pulley 18 inches by 4 inches. Pulley 11 inches by 3 inches. Two feet 6 inches of $1^3/_8$ inch shaft, Two plummer blocks, One pulley to conveyor 10 inches by 3 inches. Elevator with wood heads. top and bottom pulleys and spindles. 25 feet of double spouting, 54 feet about Roller belt cups 4 inches wide fixed on ditto. Flour mixer with beater, 2 feet of $1^3/_4$ inch Shafting. Two plummer blocks and brasses. Two pulleys 4 inches by 3 inches. Wood spout 6 feet 6 inches by 15 inches by $13^1/_2$ inches. One flour mixer with crank shaft connecting rod — pulleys 8 inches by $2^1/_2$ inches and 7 inches by $2^1/_2$ inches. Two plummer blocks in wood fixings hangers and spout to conveyor.

Stone Floor A No. 1 size "Eureka" smut machine with sifter — 7 feet 6 inches of $2^1/_2$ inch Shafting being an addition in length made to existing shaft. One post bracket plummer block One pulley 14 inches by 3 inches in halves. One pair bevel wheels about 20 inches and 12 inches diameter with wood and iron cogs pitched and trimmed. $1^1/_2$ feet of 2 $^1/_4$ inch turned upright shaft. Two plummer blocks and brasses for ditto, One foot step pedestal with brass step, 37 feet run (about) of Fir Scantling in posts and brays. Sundry bolts and nuts and screws securing same. One pulley 40 inches by 5 inches, driving smutter, 26 feet run (about) small scantling with wrought iron strap and wall bolt for smutter fixing. Feed spout to smutter Discharge spout from ditto. Discharge spout from sifter. Elevator with iron bottom and wood head with 14 inches by $4^1/_2$ inches internal pulleys spindles bearings and tightening screws 23 feet double spouting 50 feet webbing with 4 inch buckets thereon. Pulley 18 inches by 4 inches Fir bray with bolts and nuts. Feed spout 11 feet long to Elevator bottoms. Discharge spout $5^1/_2$ feet long. Iron proof staff and cover. Grindstone with wood frame trough pulley and hand cranks. One four inch vice as fixed. Three stone wedges. Two stone bearers. Two wood rolls. One block. Two saddle pieces. One sack barrow. Crow bar. Eye rape. Pair 4 inch iron sheave blocks. 40 feet rope for ditto. Five iron bolts. Two floor timbers for stones. Two wood spouts. One stone tracer. Eight furrow splines and triangle level Mahogany stone staff and oak stone staff. Spout hoe. Strap paste box. Two Brooms and hand brush, 2

172

feet 9 inches of $1^3/_8$ shaft with collars and set of screws for sifter gear Two hanging carriages for ditto. One pulley (block) 19 inches by $2^1/_2$ inches. One Pulley (turned) $7^1/_2$ inches by 4 inches. Two sets of strap guides. Rolls and frames as fixed. Wood pulley 9 inches by 3 inches. Iron pulley 10 inches by 2 inches double flange 1 foot 10 inches of $1^3/_4$ inch shaft. Two plummer blocks. Two wood hanging brackets for carrying plummer blocks. Two pairs of coupling. One plummer block and brasses. One wood bearing. Wood pulley 18 inches by 7 inches. Wood pulley 24 inches by 4 inches flanged. *Lower Floor* One sifter 8 feet by 1 foot 10 inches suspended under floor with crankshaft Two plummer blocks, connecting rod, delivery hopper and with two sleeves and feeding spout Length of sack hoist chain, lever sack jigger with hopper 2 feet by 12 inches by 12 inches, iron slip and sack sleeve. One spout 1 foot 6 inches by 9 inches by 9 inches with sack sleeves and cords. One lever sack jigger with sleeve and cords as fixed. Cupboard with shelf and partitions Two shelves as fixed to wall. One moveable desk. Four feed pins and cords for stones. Four sack holders with hooks and cords. Portable weighing machine. Two feed cords and slips. Meal shovel. 18 inches round sieves, hand scoop, Meal scuttle. Oil feeder. Screw spanners, 4 spanners, Two hand brushes, Two oil can, Two candlesticks. Wood block and box. Meal conveyor 14 feet long 30 feet by 3 inches. Belt with hoes thereon. Four plummer blocks with brasses and oil cups. Spindles and pulleys 4 feet 6 inches of $1^1/_2$ inch upright shaft One plummer block and one foot step. Wood pulley 4 feet by 4 inches pair of bevel wheels 2 feet 6 inches of $1^1/_4$ inch shaft. 2 plummer blocks. Two pulleys. 15 inch diameter for Governor. Head pump with suction and delivery pipe to cog pit.

List of Straps Main strap. Two silk machine straps. Elevator strap. Two mixer straps. Fan strap. Smutter strap. Sifter strap. Two odd straps. One Grindstone strap. Four wheat cleaner straps. Governor strap. Conveyor strap. Exhaust apparatus as applied to 3 pairs of stones comprising iron exhaust fan fixed on floor driving and driven pulleys spout to stive chamber. Exhaust truck over stones with iron sockets and slides exhaust spouts from vats-eye closer as fixed to dust boards, ventilating shaft with revolving ventilator. Dynamo as fixed in Mill and House for lighting purposes.

NOTE: The above extract has been produced from a photocopy of the original hand-written Indenture which has some unusual spelling and a shortage of punctuation, the latter intentional being part of a legal document.

Appendix D
Local Millwrights

The two firms which are readily called to mind and which functioned especially in East Anglia are Whitmore and Binyon of Wickham Market, Suffolk and E.R. & F. Turner of Ipswich, Suffolk.

The Wickham Market Ironworks were established by Mr. Whitmore in 1780. The firm prospered and were very well-known in the milling world. It became Whitmore & Binyon in 1868 and specialised in milling and mining machinery at an early date. They were responsible for installations in a great many mills, some being the largest in the country. They also exported a considerable amount of machinery for milling rice as well as corn.

Insofar as the Waveney Valley is concerned. Whitmore & Binyon designed a flow for a 2-sack Roller Plant at Earsham Mill and no doubt installed it. There are no records of their work in other mills but that is not to say Earsham Mill was the only mill they dealt with.

E.R. & F. Turner also had a hand in mill machinery installation in at least one Waveney Valley mill. They provided a detailed estimate for a $1/_2$ to 1 sack Roller Plant in Bungay Mill for Mr. Charles Marston. They too could well have supplied and installed machinery in other Waveney Mills.

A more locally situated firm of milling engineers who provided waterwheels and gearing to mills on the River Waveney was Messrs. E.H. Knights & Sons of London Road, Harleston. The exact date of their establishment has been difficult to ascertain but it is known they were in business in 1858. They are now owned by Farm & Country Ltd. of Bury St. Edmunds, Suffolk. The firm have traded under the following names since 1858:-

1858	Knights & Woolnough, Millwrights, Harleston.[1]
1863–1879	Robert Knights, Engineer, Millwright and iron and brass founder. Later also agricultural implement maker. Foundry, London Road, Harleston. [2]
1883–1888	Knights & Stacey, Engineers & Millwrights, London Road, Harleston.[3]
1900	Arthur John Estcourt, Millwright, London Road, Harleston & Corn Exchange, Norwich, Edward H. Knights, foreman.[4]
1916	Edward H. Knights, Engineer & Millwright, London Road, Harleston.[5]
1933–1937	Edward Knights & Sons, Engineers, London Road, Harleston.[6]

There are two wooden gear wheel templates remaining out of a great many that at one time were stored in the premises. These were photographed by the writer and are reproduced in the text. The double or composite gear wheel template on the left has a removable top section which is $30^1/_4$ ins. diameter excluding teeth and $33^1/_4$ ins. including the 49 teeth. The lower or larger section is $34^3/_4$ ins. diameter excluding teeth, and 44 ins. diameter including the 57 teeth. The thickness of the gear wheel is $3^1/_4$ ins. excluding the depth of the guide arms for the top section and hub, a total of another 3 ins. The bevel gear wheel template, on the right, is 38 ins. diameter, width of bevel $5^1/_4$ ins, 61 teeth and the bevel $2^1/_2$ ins. thick.

The two templates have no dates on them or the maker's initials, which is unusual. It is thought they were probably made in the early years of the present century. It is not recorded exactly what such gears would be used for but there is little doubt the templates were used to produce milling machinery.

MILLWRIGHTS

1. Kelly's Directory.
2. Kelly's Directory and Harrod's Directory.
3. Kelly's Directory.
4. Ibid.
5. Ibid.
6. Kelly's Directories.

Glossary

This is a list of terms associated with milling, especially in watermills. Only a small number are used in this book, but they could well be found in other literature on the subject or when visiting mills open to the public.

Ark — Bin for storage of grain or meal.

Arms — The spokes of a gear or water wheel.

Aspirator — Machine for cleaning grain before it enters the grinding system. It is effected by means of a fan which draws out dust and impurities.

Axle Tree — The wooden shaft on which a waterwheel is mounted. Later cast iron replaced wood.

Back Watering — The braking effect caused by the immersion of the lowest paddles or floats of a waterwheel in the tail race.

Balance Weights — Lead weights inserted into inset boxes, usually iron, in the top of runner stones to achieve balance. This is comparable to balancing the wheels of a motor vehicle.

Bedstone — The stationary or lower stone of a pair; also known as a ligger.

Bell Alarm — A warning bell indicating there is lack of grain in the hopper.

Bill — See Mill-Bill.

Bins — The compartments for storing grain on the top floor of the mill; also known as the bin, garner or granary floor.

Bist — A bran filled sack used as a cushion to kneel on or to support the elbow when stone dressing.

Blades — See Floats.

Blue Stone — See Cullin stone.

Bollard — The horizontal barrel of a sack hoist.

Bolter — A device for dressing flour utilising a revolving cylindrical frame covered with a fabric known as a Bolting Cloth, originally wool, then calico and later silk, through which the flour is shaken.

Bosom — The depression round the edge of the eye of the revolving or runner stone.

Brayer — The hinged bridge-tree raised or depressed by a screw nut, whereby tentering, or adjustment of the gap between the stones is effected.

Breast-shot Wheel — A wheel where the water is projected at or against it at axle level.

Bridge Tree — The beam on which there is a footstep bearing of the stone spindle.

Bridging Box — An adjustable housing for a footstep bearing.

Buckets — Fittings, variously shaped, around the waterwheel for receiving the water.

Burr stone — A millstone made from a freshwater quartz quarried in the Paris basin; often referred to as a French Burr stone.

Centrifugal Reel Separator — A device for dressing flour by means of a cylinder with an independent set of arms or beaters arranged to rotate within the silk covering. The material fed into the machine is thrown with a certain force against the silk cover. A Prussian millwright named Martin claims to have invented the centrifugal dressing machine.

Clasp Arm Wheel — A wooden wheel with two pairs of parallel spokes forming a cruciform frame and a square around the shaft or axle.

Compass Arm Wheel — A timber wheel with radiating spokes mortised to the axle or shaft.

Composition Stones — Millstones made from cement and carborundum and other abrasive materials.

Cracking — The cutting of fine grooves in the surface of the lands of a millstone. Referred to as drills, feathering or stitching.

Crock String — The string or cord used to regulate the opening from the hopper to the shoe.

Crown Wheel — A bevel gear wheel at the top of the upright shaft, engaging pinions for driving ancillary machinery in the mill via layshafts and pulleys.

Cullin Stone — A millstone of volcanic lava from Germany which used to be shipped from Cologne.

Damsel — A device made of wrought iron which is rotated by the stone spindle on underdriven stones. It agitates the shoe thus assisting the flow of grain into the eye of the stone. So named for the similarity of its chattering to that of women!

Derbyshire Peaks — Millstones quarried in one piece in the Derbyshire Peak District.

Dressing Machines — Used to separate the meal into various grades of flour and animal feed.

Dressing Stones — The act of cutting the furrows, lands and stitching in stones when new or worn.

Edge Runner Stones — Stones which rotate in a vertical plane, the edge forming the crushing surface.

Elevator — An arrangement for carrying grain, etc., vertically in the mill. It consists of an endless belt to which are fixed receptacles, all of which is enclosed in a wooden casing. It is powered from the crown wheel.

Eye — The hole in the centre of the runner or revolving stone through which grain passes into the stones.

Face Wheel — A gear wheel with cogs on the face or flat of the wheel instead of the outer edge where they project radially from the centre.

False Board — The upper section of an inclined hatch or sluice gate used with Undershot and Poncelet type wheels.

Felloe — The section of the rim of a wooden wheel.

Fer-de-Moline — Heraldic term for a mill rynd.

Flaunch or Flanch — A circular metal plate on the hub or rim of a waterwheel to which arms are bolted.

Floats — The wood or metal blades or paddles of a waterwheel.

Flood Hatch or Gate — The sluice for diverting water from the waterwheel to the overflow or spillway stream.

Flour Dresser — See Bolter and Centrifugal Reel Separator.

Flume — A leat or channel, usually man-made, conveying headrace water to the wheel; also known as lade.

Footstep Bearing — A bearing at the lower end of an upright shaft.

French Burr Stone — See Burr Stone.

Fulling Mill — One in which woven cloth is shrunk and dressed.

Furrows — The main grooves cut in the grinding surface of a millstone to lead the meal to the outer edge.

Garner — The top floor of a mill where grain is stored; also known as the Bin Floor or Granary Floor.

Gate — A control which regulates the flow of water to a water wheel.

Gimbal — The balancing ring supporting a runner stone.

Governor — An automatic device to assist in regulating the distance between the stones.

Gradual Reduction — Production of flour by multiple reduction.

Great Spur Wheel — The spur wheel mounted on the main vertical shaft transmitting the drive to the mill stones via the stone nuts and spindles.

Grist — Any material ground in a mill; latterly it refers to the grinding of animal feed stuffs.

Gudgeon — An iron pin or pivot at the end of a shaft or axle forming a bearing.

Hackle Plate — A square cover plate over the spindle bearing in a bed stone.

Hackle Screws — Adjusting screws utilised when remounting a runner stone.

Harp — Segment of the grinding surface of a millstone which contains lands and furrows.

Hatch — See Gate.

Head Race — Stream of water above the mill; often referred to as leat.

Headsill or Sill — The top of the wall to a weir or dam.

High Breast Wheel — A wheel where the water is projected at or against it above axle level.

High Milling — The process of grinding grain several times by gradual reduction.

Hopper — An inverted pyramid shaped wooden container placed above the millstones and into which grain is fed from the bin floor by gravity. It controls the discharge of grain to the millstones via the shoe.

Horse — Wooden or iron framework with four legs supporting the hopper and shoe above the tun or vat.

Hunting Cog — An additional cog on one of two meshing gearwheels to avoid exact ratio thus preventing the same wear on each cog for every revolution.

Hurst or Hursting — Heavy timber framework, but latterly metal, supporting the millstones.

Hurstle — See Tun.

Hutch — A corn bin in the loft of a mill.

Jack Ring — An iron frame for lifting the stone nut out of gear.

Jockey Pulley — A small pulley used to tension a belt.

Joggling Screen or Jog Scry — An inclined oscillating sieve for sifting partly ground corn before a second grinding; also called a Jumper.

Lade — See Flume.

Lands — The flat parts of the grinding surfaces of millstones.

Lantern Pinion — An early form of wooden gear wheel consisting of staves set between two discs.

Launder — A wooden or iron trough carrying water to a waterwheel.

Layshaft — An intermediate shaft transmitting power via pulleys to additional equipment including a sack hoist.

Leat — See Head Race

Ligger — See Bedstone

Lightening Tree — An adjustable wooden shaft in a Greek or Norse Mill used to vary the distance between the stones via the Sole Tree.

Low Breast Wheel — A wheel where water is projected at or against it at a point below the axle level.

Low Milling — The traditional method of producing flour by a single operation, i.e., by passing the grain once through the stones.

Lucam — A projecting dormer in the roof of a watermill with sack trap doors through which sacks of grain can be lifted by the sack hoist to the Bin, Garner or Granary floor.

Mace Head — The head mounted on the tip end of a stone spindle driving and/or supporting the gimbal.

Magnetic Separator — A device for removing stray pieces of metal from grain prior to grinding. Introduced in the latter part of the 19th century.

Meal Floor — The floor below the millstones to which flour was discharged into bins.

Meal Spout — A chute through which meal or flour is conveyed from the stones to sacks.

Middlings — An intermediate product from the flour dresser used for a coarse 'household' bread but mainly for pig and cattle food.

Mill-Bill — The implement used to dress the stones comprising a handle or 'thrift' and a double-ended wedge-shaped steel tool.

Miller's Willow — A twig used to form a return spring to the shoe.

Mill-Eye — A chute for flour as it leaves the skirting of the stones.

Mill Race — The stream of water above the mill.

Mill Rhynd, Rynd or Rind — A metal bridge across the eye of the runner stone giving it support. An old term usually applied to the Mace Head (q.v.).

Mill Staff — A straight edge, usually of mahogany, used for testing the surface of a millstone when dressing. Used with red-oxide paint to ascertain the high spots. Also called a Paint Staff.

Millstones — The circular stones used to grind the grain and comprising the Bed, Nether or Stationary Stone and the Upper or Runner Stone.

Mortised Wheel — An iron wheel with wooden cogs or teeth mortised in.

Nether Stone — See Bedstone.

Overdrift Millstones — Stones driven from above.

Overshot Wheel — A wheel where water is taken to a point just past top dead centre and thence into the buckets.

Paddles — See Floats; also a metal plate fixed to the runner stone for sweeping the meal around the inside of the vat to the meal hole in the floor.

Peak Stone — See Derbyshire Peaks.

Penstock — A device, such as a sluice gate, for controlling water to a wheel, or alternatively a wooden or metal trough carrying water to the wheel.

Pitwheel — The first gear wheel inside the mill usually iron and sometimes with wooden teeth or cogs. It is mounted on the same shaft as the waterwheel and is therefore parallel to it.

Pitchback Wheel — A wheel where water is taken to a point just before top dead centre and thence to the buckets. It therefore revolves in the opposite direction to that of an Overshot wheel.

Plansifter — A machine equipped with a number of horizontal sieves placed one on top of the other and used for dressing flour.

Pollards — A coarse by-product of flour milling consisting largely of fine bran and bran powder mixed with tailings.

Poncelet Wheel — A type of undershot waterwheel developed by the French General J.V. Poncelet.

Proof-Staff — A steel straight-edge for checking the Mill Staff (q.v.)

Provender Milling — The preparation of feeding stuffs for live stock.

Purifier — A machine combining the use of sieves and air blowing to separate the endosperm from the bran thus producing a fine flour.

Quant — The iron spindle carrying the stone nut for driving an overdrift millstone.

Race — A channel of water to or from the waterwheel.

Raddle — Paint composed of red oxide and water which is applied to the mill or paint staff to detect the high spots on grinding surfaces of stones prior to dressing.

Reel — The frame carrying the silk sleeve in a Bolter (q.v.).

Rhynd, Rynd or Rind — See Mill Rhynd.

Rigger — A band wheel or pulley driving belting.

Rim Gearing — A toothed rack on the inside rim of a waterwheel meshing with a pinion providing a direct drive via a separate shaft.

Roller Mill — One that is equipped with steel rollers for grinding in place of traditional stones.

Rung — An old term for a float or paddle.

Runner Stone — The upper millstone which revolves.

Sack Chain — The chain used for hoisting sacks of grain.

Sack Hoist — A device for raising sacks of grain up to the various floors of the mill.

Screener — A machine used for removing dust and dirt from grain prior to grinding.

Separator — A machine used in place of or in conjunction with a screener.

Shelling — The removal of husks from oats prior to grinding.

Shoe — A small inclined trough which feeds grain from the hopper to the eye of the runner stone. It is agitated by the damsel to keep the grain moving.

Shroud — The outer vertical casing at the circumference of a breast shot, overshot or pitchback waterwheel to enclose the buckets or floats.

Shuttle — A sluice.

Sickle Dress — Method of stone dressing using curved radiating furrows.

Silk Machine — A device for dressing flour through a tube of silk by means of revolving brushes.

Skirt — The outer edge of a millstone.

Slip Cogs — Removable cogs to allow a pinion to be taken out of gear.

Sluice — A gate which can be raised or lowered to control the flow or level of water.

Smutter — A machine for removing smut, a fungal growth common in wheat.

Sole Plate — The lower board of a bucket on a waterwheel or the lining of a waterwheel.

Sole Tree — The lower beam in framework supporting the stones in a Greek or Norse mill.

Spattle — A sliding shutter to control the flow of grain from hopper to shoe.

Spur Wheel — See Great Spur Wheel.

Starter Box — A metal tank filled with water, placed above a waterwheel and used to set it in motion.

Starts — Short lengths of wood or metal acting as stays which project from the rim of a waterwheel to support the floats or buckets.

Steelyard — An iron lever linking the governor to the brayer (q.v.) via the tentering screw and therefore part of the tentering mechanism.

Stitching — See Cracking.

Stone Casing — Removable circular or octagonal wooden casing enclosing a pair of millstones.

Stone Crane — A device used to raise and turn over the runner stone when it requires dressing.

Stone Dresser — A craftsman who prepares the working surfaces of millstones.

Stone Nut — The small gear wheel or pinion which engages with the Great Spur Wheel(q.v.) and transmits power via the stone spindle to drive the millstone.

Stone Spindle — A shaft supporting and driving the runner stone.

Tail Race — The waterway carrying water from the wheel.

Temse — A hand sieve for dressing flour.

Tentering Gear — The mechanism for automatically controlling the space or distance between the stones through the means of a governor, steelyard and brayer. It also provides for an adjustment to be made by hand by operating a thumb screw.

Thrift — A wooden handle, usually of ash, into which the mill bill is held and wedged.

Tiver — See Raddle.

Trunnion — A bearing at the end of a shaft.

Tide Mill — A watermill utilising the rise and fall of the tide at the river mouth or estuary. It has a mill pond in the form of a tidal pond or reservoir.

Trough — See Launder.

Trundle Wheel — See Lantern Pinion.

Tucking Mill — Another term for a Fulling Mill (q.v.).

Tun — See Stone Casing.

Turbine — A highly efficient device whereby water power is utilised in conditions where a conventional waterwheel would either be unsuitable or not provide sufficient power. Water is directed on to vanes of an enclosed wheel which rotates in a horizontal plane. Usually fitted to Roller Mills.

Twist Peg — A wooden peg to which the cord that controls the flow of grain from the shoe into the eye of the millstone is attached.

Underdrift Millstones — Stones driven from beneath.

Upright Shaft — The vertical shaft on which are mounted the Wallower, Great Spur Wheel and Crown Wheel.

Vat — See Stone Casing.

Ventilating Buckets — Waterwheel buckets designed with a gap between the top of the inside of one bucket and the back of the following bucket so as to enable air to escape and thus allow the water to enter more quickly. The buckets therefore received the maximum weight of water in the shortest time which increased the efficiency of Breastshot, Overshot and Pitchback wheels.

Vertical Mill — The traditional European mill driven by a vertical waterwheel.

Vertical Shaft — See Upright Shaft.

Vitruvian Mill — The mill described by the Roman architect and engineer, Marcus Vitruvius between 20 and 11 BC, and the forerunner of European vertical mills.

Wallower — The lower bevelled gear wheel on the upright shaft used to transmit power from the pitwheel. In the Vitruvian Mill a lantern pinion was used as a wallower.

Weir — A dam across a stream or river to divert water to a mill or to maintain it at the required height.

Widdershins — The method of dressing stones against the sun or left-handed.

Winnower — A fan which blows dust, etc., from the grain as it descends a chute.

Winter Mill — One that is mentioned in the Domesday Survey and which could only be used during winter months when water became available in the usually small stream.

Wire Machine — An alternative to the Bolter (q.v.), in which there was a stationary cylinder covered with wire gauze and enclosed in a wooden box-like structure. The cylinder was placed at an inclined position over a series of hoppers, usually five. The finest wire was at the upper end, the meshes increasing in size towards the lower end where bran was discharged. Meal was delivered to the top of the cylinder by a wooden spout and was driven through the wire mesh by internal revolving brushes. Various grades of flour was then obtained as well as middlings (q.v.) and pollards (q.v.).

Suggested Further Reading

Apling, Harry, Norfolk Corn Windmills, Vol. I, 1984.

Benham, Hervey, Some Essex Watermills, 1976.

Bennett, Richard and John Elton, History of Cornmilling, Vol. II, Watermills and Windmills, 1973 (fascimile reprint of the 1899 Edition); Vol. IV, Some Feudal Mills, 1975 (fascimile reprint of the 1904 Edition) by E.P. Publishing Ltd.

Brown, R.J., Windmills of England, 1976.

Buchanan, R.A., Industrial Archaeology in Britain 1972.

Burnett, R.G., Through the Mill, The Life of Joseph Rank, 1945.

Finch, William Coles, Watermills and Windmills, 1933.

Hills, Richard L., Papermaking in Britain 1488–1988, A Short History, 1988.

Hopkins, R. Thurston, Old Watermills and Windmills, 1934.

Hudson, Kenneth, Industrial Archaeology, An Introduction, 1963.

Lewis, Paul, The Romance of Water Power, c.1930.

Long, George, The Mills of Man, 1931.

Raistrick, Arthur, Industrial Archaeology, An Historial Survey 1972.

Reid, K.C. Watermills of the London Countryside, I, 1987, and II, 1989.

Reynolds, John, Windmills and Watermills, 1970.

Shorter, Dr. A.H., Papermaking in the British Isles, An Historical and Georgraphical Study, 1971.

Skilton, C.P., British Windmills and Watermills, 1947.

Stidder, Derek, The Watermills of Surrey, 1990.

Storck & Teague, Flour for Man's Bread, 1952.

Strandh, Sigvard, A History of the Machine, 1984.

Syson, Leslie, British Watermills, 1965.

Syson, Leslie, The Watermills of Britain, 1980.

Vince, John, Discovering Watermills, 1970.

Vince, John, Power Before Steam, 1985.

Wenham, Peter, Watermills 1989.

Publications of the Wind and Watermill Section of the Society for the Protection of Ancient Buildings:-

Gardner, E.M., Tide Mills, Part III, 1956.

Luckhurst, D., Monastic Watermills.

Pelham, Dr. R.A., Fulling Mills, 1956.

Reid, K.C. Watermills and the Landscape, 1959.

Rollins, J.G., Needle Mills, 1970.

Shorter, Dr. A.H., Water Paper Mills, 1966.

Wailes, Rex, Tide Mills, Parts I and II, 1956.

Wailes, Rex. Suffolk Watermills, 1965.
Lord Wilson of High Wray, Watermills — An Introduction, 1956, Revised 1970.
Wilson, P.N.,(later Lord Wilson of High Wray),Watermills with Horizontal Wheels, 1960.

Index

THE RIVER WAVENEY,

WATERMILLS

AND LOCKS.

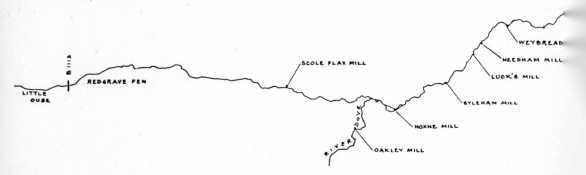